Edexcel Award in
Number &
Measure

Level
1

WORKBOOK

Bobbie Johns

PEARSON

Published by Pearson Education Limited, Edinburgh Gate, Harlow, Essex, CM20 2JE.

www.pearsonschoolsandfecolleges.co.uk

Text © Pearson Education Limited 2013
Edited by Project One Publishing Solutions, Scotland
Typeset and illustrated by Tech-Set Ltd, Gateshead
Original illustrations © Pearson Education Limited 2013
Cover image © AXL / Shutterstock.com

The right of Bobbie Johns to be identified as author of this work has been asserted by her in accordance with the Copyright, Designs and Patents Act 1988.

First published 2013

17 16 15 14 13
10 9 8 7 6 5 4 3 2 1

British Library Cataloguing in Publication Data
A catalogue record for this book is available from the British Library

ISBN 978 1 446 90327 8

Printed in Slovakia by Neografia

Acknowledgements
Every effort has been made to contact copyright holders of material reproduced in this book. Any omissions will be rectified in subsequent printings if notice is given to the publishers.

Disclaimer
This material has been published on behalf of Edexcel and offers high-quality support for the delivery of Edexcel qualifications.

This does not mean that the material is essential to achieve any Edexcel qualification, nor does it mean that it is the only suitable material available to support any Edexcel qualification. Material from this publication will not be used verbatim in any examination or assessment set by Edexcel. Any resource lists produced by Edexcel shall include this and other appropriate resources.

Copies of official specifications for all Edexcel qualifications may be found on the Edexcel website: www.edexcel.com

In the writing of this book, no Edexcel examiners authored sections relevant to examination papers for which they have responsibility.

Notices

The calculator symbol 🖩 shows questions where:
- calculator skills are being developed, or
- using a calculator effectively is an important aspect of answering the question, or
- the calculation exceeds the scope of written methods in earlier chapters.

The calculator symbol does NOT imply that the subject area covered by the question will ONLY appear on the calculator section, Section A, of the paper.

You may wish to use a calculator in some chapters to facilitate calculations at your teacher's discretion.

Remember: Almost every concept and skill may be tested in every paper.

The GCSE links provide references to course books as follows:
AF Edexcel GCSE Mathematics A Foundation Student Book
BF Edexcel GCSE Mathematics B Foundation Student Book
16+ Edexcel GCSE Mathematics 16+ Student Book

Contents

Self-assessment chart

	Needs more practice	Almost there	I'm proficient!	Notes
Chapter 1 Integers				
1.1 Read, write, order and compare positive integers	☐	☐	☐	
1.2 Add and subtract positive integers	☐	☐	☐	
1.3 Multiply and divide by 10, 100 and 1000	☐	☐	☐	
1.4 Multiplication and division facts up to 10×10	☐	☐	☐	
1.5 Multiply and divide by a single digit	☐	☐	☐	
1.6 Round to the nearest 10, 100 and 1000	☐	☐	☐	
1.7 Find multiples and factors and identify prime numbers	☐	☐	☐	
1.8 Understand and use negative numbers	☐	☐	☐	
Chapter 2 Decimals				
2.1 Read, write and order decimals	☐	☐	☐	
2.2 Add and subtract decimals	☐	☐	☐	
2.3 Multiply and divide decimal numbers	☐	☐	☐	
2.4 Rounding decimals	☐	☐	☐	
Chapter 3 Checking and approximation				
3.1 Check solutions	☐	☐	☐	
Chapter 4 Fractions				
4.1 Read, write and order fractions	☐	☐	☐	
4.2 Use equivalent fractions	☐	☐	☐	
4.3 Write fractions in their simplest form	☐	☐	☐	
4.4 Convert between fractions and decimals	☐	☐	☐	
4.5 Add and subtract fractions	☐	☐	☐	
4.6 Find fractions of quantities	☐	☐	☐	
Chapter 5 Percentages				
5.1 Decimals, fractions and percentages	☐	☐	☐	
5.2 Order and compare percentages	☐	☐	☐	
5.3 Find percentages of quantities	☐	☐	☐	
Chapter 6 Money				
6.1 Read and order amounts of money	☐	☐	☐	
6.2 Calculating with money	☐	☐	☐	
Chapter 7 Time				
7.1 Read, record and measure time	☐	☐	☐	
7.2 Use units of time	☐	☐	☐	
7.3 Convert between units of time	☐	☐	☐	
7.4 Use calendars	☐	☐	☐	
Chapter 8 Measures				
8.1 Metric and imperial measures	☐	☐	☐	
8.2 Convert between metric units	☐	☐	☐	
8.3 Add and subtract units of measure	☐	☐	☐	
8.4 Read scales	☐	☐	☐	
8.5 Draw and measure lines and angles	☐	☐	☐	
Chapter 9 Area and perimeter				
9.1 Perimeter of rectangles	☐	☐	☐	
9.2 Area of rectangles	☐	☐	☐	
Chapter 10 Volume				
10.1 Volume of cuboids	☐	☐	☐	
Chapter 11 Tables and charts				
11.1 Read and interpret real-life charts	☐	☐	☐	
11.2 Read bar charts and dual bar charts	☐	☐	☐	
11.3 Draw bar charts	☐	☐	☐	

1.1 Read, write, order and compare positive integers

By the end of this section you will know how to:

* Read, write, order and compare positive integers up to 1000

GCSE LINKS
AF: 1.1 Place value, 1.2 Reading, writing, ordering;
BF: Unit 2 1.1 Place value, 1.2 Reading, writing, ordering

Key points

* The value of each digit depends on its place in the number.
* A 3-digit whole number is always larger than a 2-digit whole number.

> **Remember this**
> An **integer** is a positive or negative whole number including zero.

Guided

1 a Read and write **456** in words.

Hundreds	Tens	Units
4	5	6
400	50	6

= four .... and .... – ....

b Read and write **509** in words.

Hundreds	Tens	Units
5	0	9
....	0	....

= ....

2 Write these numbers in words. Use the words in question 1 to help you.

a 274 .... hundred and ....

b 350 three .... and ....

c 605 ....

d 418 ....

e 999 ....

> **Remember this**
> Writing a number in figures is the same as writing it in numerals or digits.

Practice

3 Write these numbers in figures.

a four hundred and ninety-seven ....

b three hundred and nineteen ....

c eight hundred and three ....

d nine hundred and thirty ....

Guided

4 Partition (split up) these numbers into hundreds, tens and units.

a 386 = 300 + ...0.... + ...

b 405 = 4............ + ... + ...

c 710 = ... + ... + ...

d 942 = ... + ... + ...

Practice

5 Partition these numbers.

a 829 ....

b 471 ....

c 620 ....

d 706 ....

Comparing and ordering numbers

Guided

6 Use the words 'is greater than' or 'is less than' to compare these numbers.

a 27 is less than 45

b 81 is .... than 78

c 48 is 51

d 376 457

e 730 489

f 701 699

Practice

7 Write these numbers in order.

a 465   639   285   313   smallest .... largest

b 673   763   637   736   smallest .... largest

c 451   423   432   415   largest .... smallest

8 a What is the largest number you can make with the digits ④, ⑨ and ③?

b What is the smallest number you can make with the digits ④, ⑨ and ③?

c What is the nearest number to 400 you can make with the digits ④, ⑨ and ③?

Step into GCSE

9 a In the number **3756** what is the value of the 7? ....

b Write the number **4708** in words. ....

c Write the number **nine thousand, four hundred and seventeen** in numerals. ....

Needs more practice ☐   Almost there ☐   I'm proficient! ☐

1.2 Add and subtract positive integers

GCSE LINK
AF: 1.4 Adding and subtracting; BF: Unit 2 1.4 Adding and subtracting

By the end of this section you will know how to:

* Add and subtract positive integers

Key points

* Digits of the same place value must be added together.
* When adding or subtracting in columns, digits of the same place value must be lined up carefully.

1 Look for number bonds to 10 and other multiples of 10 to add these numbers.

> **You should know**
> Addition can be done in any order, but this is not true for subtraction.

a $23 + 37 = 20 + 30 + 3 + 7 = 50 +$ .... $=$ ....

b $46 + 54 = 40 +$ .... $+$ .... $+$ .... $=$ .... $+$ .... $=$ ....

c $25 + 32 + 45 = 25 + 45 + 32 =$ .... $+$ .... $+$ .... $+$ .... $+$ .... $+$ .... $=$ .... $+$ .... $=$ ....

2 Work out these subtraction calculations using a number line to help you.

a $24 - 17 =$ ....

$+3 +4 = 7$

10   17 20 24   30

b $37 - 21 =$ ....

$+$ ...... $+$ ...... $=$ ......

21   37

c $45 - 25 =$ ....

25   45

d $78 - 24 =$ ....

e $43 - 29 =$ ....

f $84 - 16 =$ ....

3 Write the pairs of numbers that add together to make 100.

81	31	19	93
79	7	59	9
21	41	91	69

.... $+$ .... $= 100$ .... $+$ .... $= 100$

.... $+$ .... $= 100$ .... $+$ .... $= 100$

.... $+$ .... $= 100$ .... $+$ .... $= 100$

4 Find the totals of these pairs of numbers by writing the digits in columns to add them.

a $254 + 462$

```
   H  T  U
   2  5  4
+  4  6  2
 ........ 1  6
   1
```

b $726 + 386$

```
   H  T  U
   7  2  6
+  3  8  6
 ........ 2
   1
```

c $477 + 65$

```
   H  T  U
   4  7  7
+     6  5
 ........ 2
   1
```

5 Add these pairs of numbers.

a $285 + 562$

b $275 + 691$

c $365 + 726$

d $864 + 69$

e $297 + 604$

f $758 + 65$

Guided

6 Work out these subtraction calculations.

a 735 − 291

H	T	U
7	¹3	5
− 2	9	1
....	4	4

b 802 − 578

H	T	U
8	0	¹2
− 5	7	8
....		4

c 317 − 64

H	T	U
3	¹1	7
−	6	4
....	5	3

Practice

7 Find the difference between these pairs of numbers.

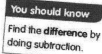

a 572 − 284

b 706 − 456

c 900 − 274

d 347 − 23

e 322 − 78

f 504 − 58

Step into GCSE

8 Work out the answers.

a In Year 10 there are 567 students and in Year 11 there are 489 students. What is the total number of students in Years 10 and 11?

....

b Sally has 821 friends on MyPals and Steve has 765. How many more friends does Sally have?

....

c Add together 265, 542 and 64.

....

4

1.3 Multiply and divide by 10, 100 and 1000

GCSE LINKS
AF: 1.5 Multiplying and dividing; BF: Unit 2 1.5 Multiplying and dividing

By the end of this section you will know how to:

* Multiply integers by 10, 100 and 1000
* Divide multiples of 10, 100 and 1000 by 10, 100 and 1000

Key points

* Multiplying a number by 10, 100 or 1000 means that each digit moves in place value to the left.
* Dividing a number by 10, 100 or 1000 means that each digit moves in place value to the right.

Guided

1 Work out the answers to these multiplications.

a $34 \times 10 = 340$

b $123 \times 10 = $ ....

c $560 \times 100 = $ ....

d $37 \times 1000 = $ ....

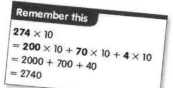

Remember this
274×10
$= 200 \times 10 + 70 \times 10 + 4 \times 10$
$= 2000 + 700 + 40$
$= 2740$

You should know
10 times table facts and related divisions.

Practice

2 Work out the answers to these multiplications.

a $57 \times 10 = $ ....

b $583 \times 10 = $ ....

c $120 \times 10 = $ ....

d $6 \times 100 = $ ....

e $72 \times 100 = $ ....

f $376 \times 100 = $ ....

g $60 \times 1000 = $ ....

h $752 \times 1000 = $ ....

i $360 \times 1000 = $ ....

Guided

3 Work out the answers to these divisions.

a $120 \div 10 = 12$

b $2650 \div 10 = $ ....

c $4800 \div 100 = $ ....

d $7000 \div 1000 = $ ....

Remember this
$270 \div 10$
$= 200 \div 10 + 70 \div 10$
$= 20 + 7$
$= 27$

Practice

4 Work out the answers to these divisions.

a $50 \div 10 = $ ....

b $290 \div 10 = $ ....

c $5000 \div 10 = $ ....

d $400 \div 100 = $ ....

e $6000 \div 100 = $ ....

f $2500 \div 100 = $ ....

g $8300 \div 100 = $ ....

h $3000 \div 1000 = $ ....

i $12\,000 \div 1000 = $ ....

5 Use the numbers in the cloud to give the answers to the following calculations.

45   4500   450   45 000

a $45 \times 10 = $ ....

b $450 \div 10 = $ ....

c $45 \times 100 = $ ....

d $4500 \div 10 = $ ....

e $4500 \div 100 = $ ....

f $45 \times 1000 = $ ....

g $45\,000 \div 1000 = $ ....

h $45\,000 \div 100 = $ ....

Step into GCSE

6 a Write a matching multiplication and division. 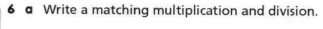 $720 = $ .... $\times$ .... $= $ .... $\div$ ....

b Fill in the missing number. $63 \times $ .... $= 6300$

c Fill in the missing number. .... $\div 1000 = 32$

5

Multiplication and division facts up to 10 × 10

By the end of this section you will know how to:

✳ Use the divisions related to multiplication facts

Key points

✳ Multiplication and division are **inverse operations**.

> **You should know**
> Multiplication can be done in any order.

Practice

1 How many of these calculations can you do in 3 minutes?

a 3 × 4 = ...   6 × 4 = ...   2 × 9 = ...   5 × 6 = ...

    7 × 3 = ...   5 × 9 = ...   4 × 7 = ...   5 × 5 = ...

    6 × 6 = ...   4 × 9 = ...   5 × 8 = ...   9 × 9 = ...

> **Hint**
> Use your answers to part **a** to help with part **b**.

b 12 ÷ 4 = ...   24 ÷ 6 = ...   18 ÷ 2 = ...   30 ÷ 6 = ...

    21 ÷ 3 = ...   45 ÷ 5 = ...   28 ÷ .... = 4   25 ÷ .... = 5

    .... ÷ 6 = 6   .... ÷ 4 = 9   .... ÷ 8 = 5   81 ÷ .... = 9

Guided

2 Write the family of four related facts.

a 4 × 5 = 20   5 × 4 = ...   20 ÷ 4 = ...   20 ÷ .... = ...

b 7 × 4 = 28   4 × .... = ...   28 ÷ .... = ...   28 ÷ .... = ...

c 15 ÷ 3 = 5   15 ÷ .... = ...   3 × .... = ... × .... = 15

> **Remember this**
> A family of related facts:
> 3 × 4 = 12
> 4 × 3 = 12
> 12 ÷ 3 = 4
> 12 ÷ 4 = 3

Practice

3 Work out the answer. Then complete the family of related facts.

a 24 ÷ 8 = ... ÷ .... = ... × .... = ... × .... = ...

b 6 × 9 = ... × .... = ... ÷ .... = ... ÷ .... = ...

c 63 ÷ 7 = ... ÷ .... = ... × .... = ... × .... = ...

Guided

4 Split the multiple of 10 into a single digit × 10 to work out the answer to these multiplications.

a 2 × 30 = 2 × 3 × 10 = ... × 10 = ...

> **Remember this**
> Multiplication by a multiple of 10 can be split up like this:
> 6 × **20** = 6 × **2** × **10** = 12 × 10 = 120

b 4 × 30 = 4 × .... × .... = ... × .... = ...

Practice

5 Work out the answers.

   a $6 \times 40 =$ ....

   b $7 \times 30 =$ ....

   c $50 \times 9 =$ ....

   d $90 \times 8 =$ ....

Step into GCSE

6 $124 \times 5 = 620$ Use this fact to find the answers.

   a $5 \times 124 =$ ....

   b $620 \div 124 =$ ....

   c $124 \times 50 =$ ....

Needs more practice ☐   Almost there ☐   I'm proficient! ☐

1.5 Multiply and divide by a single digit

GCSE LINKS
AF: 1.5 Multiplying and dividing; BF: Unit 2 1.5 Multiplying and dividing

By the end of this section you will know how to:

✳ Multiply positive integers by a single digit

✳ Divide positive integers by a single digit

Key points

✳ Numbers can be partitioned (split) into different place values to multiply them.

Guided

1 Work out the answers to these multiplications.

   a 24×5

$\times$	5
20	100
4	20

$+$

     $24 \times 5 =$ ....

   b 253×6

   c 379×4

Practice

2 Work out the answers.

   a 26×4

   b 48×3

   c 85×7

   d 218×5

   e 523×6

   f 403×9

7

Guided

3 Complete these division calculations.

a $724 \div 4 = 181$

$$4 \overline{\smash{\big)}\, 7\,^3 2\,4}$$
$$1\,8\,1$$

b $675 \div 5 =$ ....

$$5 \overline{\smash{\big)}\, 6\,7\,5}$$

c $510 \div 3 =$ ....

$$3 \overline{\smash{\big)}\, 5\,1\,0}$$

Practice

4 Work out the answers to these division calculations.

a $632 \div 4 =$ ....

b $735 \div 5 =$ ....

c $804 \div 6 =$ ....

d $486 \div 3 =$ ....

e $612 \div 9 =$ ....

f $413 \div 7 =$ ....

Step into GCSE

5 There are 240 pupils in Year 10 to be divided equally between 8 classes. How many pupils will be in each class?

....

6 a Work out $2732 \div 4$

b Work out $3366 \div 9$

....

....

Needs more practice ☐   Almost there ☐   I'm proficient! ☐

1.6 Round to the nearest 10, 100 and 1000

GCSE LINKS
AF: 1.6 Rounding;
BF: Unit 2 1.6 Rounding;
16+: 1.3 Rounding

By the end of this section you will know how to:
* Round positive integers to the nearest 10, 100 and 1000

Key points

* Round to the nearest 10: round 5, 6, 7, 8 and 9 up; round 1, 2, 3 and 4 down.
* Round to the nearest 100: round 50, 60, 70, 80 and 90 up; round 10, 20, 30 and 40 down.
* Round to the nearest 1000: round 500, 600, 700, 800 and 900 up; round 100, 200, 300 and 400 down.

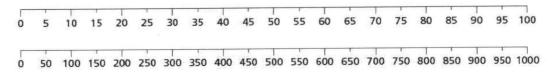

Guided

1 The table shows the distances by road from London to different cities in miles and kilometres. Round the distances in miles to the nearest 10 miles and nearest 100 miles. Use the first number line on page 8 to help you round to the nearest 10 and the second number line to help round to the nearest 100. Record your answers in the table.

Town	Distance (miles)	Nearest 10 miles	Nearest 100 miles	Distance (km)	Nearest 10 km	Nearest 100 km
Bangor	267	270	300	428		
Birmingham	118	120	00	189		
Bristol	121			193		
Cardiff	153			225		
Glasgow	405			647		
Manchester	197			314		

Practice

2 Now round the distances in question 1 to the nearest 10 km and nearest 100 km, using the number lines to help you. Record your answers in the table.

Step into GCSE

3 Look at the census form. Give an approximate population for these villages, by rounding each one to the nearest 1000. Use the number line below to help you.

Town	Population
Lakeside	2861
Fieldcourt	7239
Castle Hill	4356
Millbrook	4653
Meadow Bank	7803
Broadoak	739

Lakeside ....
Fieldcourt ....
Castle Hill ....
Millbrook ....
Meadow Bank ....
Broadoak ....

0 500 1000 1500 2000 2500 3000 3500 4000 4500 5000 5500 6000 6500 7000 7500 8000 8500 9000 9500 10 000

Needs more practice ☐   Almost there ☐   I'm proficient! ☐

1.7 Find multiples and factors and identify prime numbers

GCSE LINKS
AF: 1.10 Factors, multiples, primes, 1.11 HCF; BF: Unit 2
2.1 Factors, multiples, primes, 2.2 HCF

By the end of this section you will know how to:
* Use the terms **multiple, factor, common factor** and **prime number**

Key points

* **Factors** of a number divide into that number exactly.
* Two factors of a number that multiply together to make that number are called a **factor pair**.
* A **multiple** of a number is in the times table of that number.
* A **prime number** has only two factors — itself and 1.

Guided

1 Complete the multiplication grid. It has been started for you.

×	2	3	4	5	6	7	8	9	10
2	4	6	8		12		16	18	
3	6	9	12	15		21			30
4	8	12	16		24			36	
5			20			35			
6	12	18			36			54	
7					42		56		70
8		24	32					72	
9		27		45		63			90
10	20			50			80		

Practice

2 a Write down the multiples of 5 from the grid. ....

   b Write down the multiples of 6 from the grid. ....

   c Write down the multiples of 9 from the grid. ....

Guided

3 Find the factor pairs of 12, 30 and 16 by writing the pairs of numbers that multiply together to make that number.

a
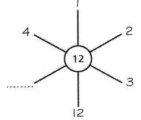

b
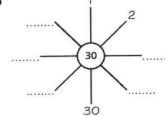

c
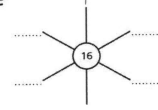

Practice

4 Use your answers in question 3 to write down the factors in order, from smallest to largest.

   a Factors of 12: ....

   b Factors of 30: ....

   c Factors of 16: ....

> **Remember this**
> You only list each number once, even if you need to multiply a number by itself to get the number in the middle.

Common factors and prime numbers

Practice

5 Look at the list of factors you made for 12, 30 and 16 in question 4. Write down the numbers that appear in both lists to show the common factors of these pairs of numbers.

   a The common factors of 12 and 30 are ....

   b The common factors of 30 and 16 are ....

   c The common factors of 12 and 16 are ....

> **Remember this**
> The **common factors** of two numbers are numbers that appear in the list of factors of both numbers.

Step into GCSE

6 Write the largest number in question 5 to show the highest common factor (HCF) of the pairs of numbers.

a The HCF of 12 and 30 is ....

b The HCF of 30 and 16 is ....

c The HCF of 12 and 16 is ....

> **Remember this**
> The **highest common factor** is often shortened to **HCF**.

Practice

7 Look at the multiplication grid on the top of page 10 and at the numbers below. Put a ring around the numbers below that do *not* appear as answers in the multiplication grid — they are prime numbers because they only appear in their own multiplication table and only have one pair of factors.

> **Remember this**
> **Prime numbers** have only two factors — the number itself and 1. 1 is not a prime number because it only has one factor.

2	3	4	5	6	7	8	9	10
11	12	13	14	15	16	17	18	19	20
21	22	23	24	25	26	27	28	29	30

Step into GCSE

8 Choose the correct number from the box.
Complete part **e** by writing a description for the numbers left over, using 'factor' or 'multiple'.

> 4   11
>   10
> 15   18
>   45

a A multiple of 6 ....

b A factor of 16 ....   c A prime number ....

d A common factor of 20 and 30 ....   e .... is a .... of ....

Needs more practice ☐   Almost there ☐   I'm proficient! ☐

1.8 Understand and use negative numbers

> **GCSE LINKS**
> AF: 1.7–1.9 Negative numbers;
> BF: Unit 2 1.7–1.9 Negative numbers; 16+: 1.1 Negative numbers

By the end of this section you will know how to:

✳ Read, order, add and subtract negative numbers

Key points

✳ Integers can be positive or negative or zero.

✳ Numbers less than zero are called **negative numbers**.

✳ In temperature a negative reading means the temperature is below zero and is very cold.

Guided

1 What temperature does each arrow show?

> **Remember this**
> Negative whole numbers and zero are also integers.

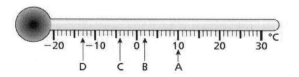

A 10°C   B .... °C   C −4°C   D .... °C

Practice

2 a Each temperature in question 1 rises by 4°. What is the new temperature?

A ....°C   B ....°C   C ....°C   D ....°C

b Each temperature in question 1 falls by 2°. What is the new temperature?

A ....°C   B ....°C   C ....°C   D ....°C

3

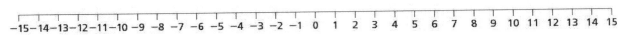

a Order these numbers from lowest to highest: 9, −4, 6, 0, −2. ....

b Order these numbers from highest to lowest: −11, 7, 0, 3, −8. ....

Guided

4 Use the number lines to help you add and subtract negative numbers.

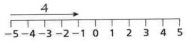   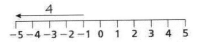

a 4 more than −5 = −1

b 4 less than −1 = ...

c 5 more than −5 = ...

d 6 less than 2 = ...

e 4 more than −1 = ...

f 3 less than −1 = ...

Step into GCSE

5 Work out the answers.

a −4 + 2 = ...

b 3 − 6 = ...

c −2 − 4 = ...

d −2 + 2 = ...

e 0 − 10 = ...

f −3 − 8 = ...

Don't forget!

✻ Draw a line to match each term with its definition.

integer	negative number	multiple of 10	factor	prime number
number that divides exactly into another number	number less than zero	whole number	number divisible only by itself and 1	number in the 10 times table

✻ Match each calculation with the correct answer.

−3 + 5	2 − 5	−5 + 3	−1 − 4
−5	−2	2	−3

✻ Match each calculation with the correct answer.

54 ÷ 6	62 × 10	8 × 9	6200 ÷ 100
72	62	9	620

✻ When rounding to the nearest hundred, if a number ends in 50, 60, 70, 80 or 90, you round ....
and if the number ends in 10, 20, 30 or 40, you round ....

Exam-style questions

1 **a** Work out   24 × 10   **b** Work out   640 ÷ 10   **c** Work out   3600 ÷ 10

....

2 **a** Work out
```
    6   5   7
+   2   9   4
_____
```
b Work out
```
    7   1   6
−   3   7   2
_____
```

3 **a** Work out   256 × 4   **b** Work out   342 ÷ 6

....

4 **a** Write the number **367** in words. ....

   b Write **367** to the nearest ten. ....   **c** Write **367** to the nearest hundred. ....

5 Write these numbers in order of size. Start with the smallest number.

   a 285, 258, 528, 399 ....   **b** 6, −3, 8, 0, −11 ....

6 Here is a list of numbers. | 6 7 9 10 12 14 15 16 19 |

   From the list

   a write two multiples of 5 ....   **b** write two prime numbers ....

   c write two factors of 24 ....   **d** write two numbers that add to 30 ....

   e a common factor of 18 and 27 ....

7 **a**   Write down the reading of each mark on the thermometer.

   A .... °C   B .... °C

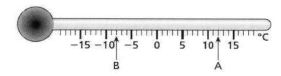

   b On thermometer C show a reading of 5°C.

   c On thermometer D show a reading of −2°C.

2.1 Read, write and order decimals

By the end of this section you will know how to:
* Read, write, order and compare decimal numbers to two decimal places
* Understand place value in relation to decimal numbers

GCSE LINKS
AF: 5.1 Decimal place value,
5.2 Ordering decimals;
BF: Unit 2 3.1 Decimal place
value, 3.2 Ordering decimals

Key points

* Place value is very important when comparing decimals with different numbers of digits after the decimal point.
* The first digit after the decimal point shows tenths and the second digit shows hundredths.

Guided

1 Write the decimal number shown in each grid.

You should know
$\frac{1}{10} = 0.1$
$\frac{1}{100} = 0.01$
$\frac{32}{100} = 0.32$

a $\frac{5}{10} = 0.$ _____

b $\frac{}{100} = 0.0$ _____

c $\frac{}{10} + \frac{}{100} =$ _____

Practice

2 Shade the grids to show the following decimal numbers.

a 0.7

b 0.04

c 0.55

d 0.62

e 0.19

f 0.91

Step into GCSE

3 Order the decimals in question 2, from smallest to largest. Use the grids to help you.

_____

Guided

4 Write in missing zeros so the numbers have the same number of decimal places. Then write them in order, from smallest to largest.

a

0.56	0.5	0.65	0.7	0.6	0.76
0.56	0.50	0.65	0.70	0.60	0.76
2nd	1st	4th	5th	3rd	6th

0.5   0.56 _____

b

2.5	2.35	2.4	2.53	2.19
2.50	2.35	2.40	2.53	2.19
				1st

2.19 _____

Practice

5 Order these decimals, starting with the smallest.

a   3.9   4.8   0.7   3.5   ....

b   3.67   4.28   3.76   4.82   ....

c   6.7   4.98   6.2   4.89   ....

d   18.7   18.75 18.6   18.58 ....

e   24.9   24.57 24.7   24.75 ....

6 Write these numbers in the correct place on the line:

5.5   6.5   7.5   5.1   6.8   7.3   6.3   7.9

5.8 has been done for you.

7 Write these numbers in the correct place on the line:

5.1   5.2   5.4   5.6   5.7   5.9   5.15

5.25   5.45   5.75   5.85   5.68   5.33   5.99

Step into GCSE

8 Write the names of the athletes to show the order in which they finished in their event. Include their times or distances.

100 m Sprint (seconds)	
B Blue	15.65
G Green	15.7
R Red	15.56
W White	15.09

Triple Jump (metres)	
T Highe	16.07
L Legge	16.5
B Speede	16.49
M Springer	15.99

Remember this

The winning time is the **shortest** time but the winning jump is the **longest** distance

a   100 m sprint: ....

b   Triple jump: ....

Needs more practice ☐   Almost there ☐   I'm proficient! ☐

Add and subtract decimals

2.2

By the end of this section you will know how to:

* Add and subtract decimal numbers

GCSE LINKS

AF: 5.3 Adding and subtracting decimals; BF: Unit 2.3.3 Adding and subtracting decimals

Key points

* Place value is very important when adding and subtracting decimals.
* To add or subtract decimals, digits with the same place value should be lined up carefully, one under the other.

Guided

1 **a** Add 3.4 and 5.8.

```
    3 . 4
  + 5 . 8
  ─────────
  ....... . 2
      |
```

b Total 5.38 and 3.92.

```
    5 . 3 8
  + 3 . 9 2
  ───────────
  ..... . ..... O
      |     |
```

c Add 14.5 and 21.56.

```
    2 1 . 5 6
  + 1 4 . 5 O
  ───────────────
  ......... . .........
```

Remember this

If you are adding numbers with different numbers of decimal places, make them the same by writing a zero in the empty place in the shorter number.

Practice

2 Work out the answers.

a 5.6 + 2.8

```
    5 . 6
  + 2 . 8
  ─────────
      .
```

b 4.68 + 2.37

```
    4 . 6 8
  + 2 . 3 7
  ───────────
      .
```

c 34.5 + 23.85

```
    3 4 . 5
  + 2 3 . 8 5
  ─────────────
      .
```

d 3.9 + 2.5

e 7.29 + 3.04

f 37 + 58.93

g 4.6 + 5.92

h 47.37 + 25.8

i 6.84 + 48.5

Step into GCSE

3 **a** Work out the total of 24.6 and 52.73.

b How much altogether is 36.7 and 42.93?

c What is 3.46 + 12.7 + 5.08?

4 Use the fact that 275 + 629 = 904 to work out 27.5 + 62.9 = ...

Guided

5 Work out the answers.

a 7.8 − 4.5

```
    7 . 8
  − 4 . 5
  ─────────
  ..... . 3
```

b 37.72 − 15.56

```
    3 7 . 7 ¹2
  − 1 5 . 5 6
  ─────────────
  ..... . ..... 6
```

c 7.3 − 5.18

```
    7 . 3 ¹0
  − 5 . 1 8
  ─────────────
  ....... . .........
```

16

Practice

6 Work out these decimal subtractions.

  a 21.6 − 15.4   **b** 45.19 − 23.81   **c** 34.27 − 19.47

  d 56.8 − 25.37   **e** 72.6 − 26.45   **f** 62.34 − 37.9

  g 69.04 − 16.73   **h** 20.37 − 14.09   **i** 64.1 − 12.07

Step into GCSE

7 a How much more than 27.3 is 76.19?

  b What is the difference between 56.28 and 83.7?

  You should know — In mathematics find the **difference** by subtracting.

  c What is 5.67 + 14.93 − 8.6?

  Hint — Do the addition first, then the subtraction.

8 Find the pairs of numbers that add to 10.

2.75	6.5	6.8	7.3
0.75	3.65	3.15	4.5
3.2	2.7	7.25	9.25
6.85	5.5	6.35	3.5

.... + ... = 10   .... + ... = 10
.... + ... = 10   .... + ... = 10
.... + ... = 10   .... + ... = 10
.... + ... = 10   .... + ... = 10

17

2.3 Multiply and divide decimal numbers

GCSE LINKS
AF: 5.4 Multiplying decimals,
5.6 Dividing decimals;
BF: Unit 2 3.4 Multiplying
decimals, 3.6 Dividing
decimals; 16+ 1.2 Decimals

By the end of this section you will know how to:
* Multiply and divide with decimal numbers
* Use a calculator to multiply and divide with decimals
* Multiply and divide numbers and decimals by 10 and 100

You should know
How to multiply and divide whole numbers by a single digit without a calculator.

Key points

* You can use whole number multiplication and division facts to multiply and divide with decimals.
* When multiplying or dividing by 10 or 100, the same rules apply to decimals and whole numbers.

Remember this
$12 \times 2 = 24$, so $1.2 \times 2 = 2.4$;
$24 \div 2 = 12$, so $2.4 \div 2 = 1.2$

Guided

1 Use whole number calculations to work out the decimal multiplications.

a $15 \times 3 = 45$ so $1.5 \times 3 =$ ....   b $24 \times 2 = 48$ so $2.4 \times$ ..... = ...

c $11 \times 5 =$ .....   so ..... $\times 5 =$ .....   d $18 \times 4 =$ .....   so ..... $\times$ ..... = ...

e $132 \times 2 =$ .....   so $13.2 \times 2 =$ .....   f $243 \times 2 =$ .....   so ..... $\times 2 =$ .....

2 Use whole number calculations to work out the decimal divisions.

a $26 \div 2 = 13$ so $2.6 \div 2 =$ .....   b $24 \div 3 =$ .....   so $2.4 \div$ ..... = 0.....

c $35 \div 5 =$ .....   so ..... $\div 5 =$ .....   d $28 \div 4 =$ .....   so ..... $\div$ ..... = ...

Practice

3 Use known number facts to work out these decimal calculations.

a $3.2 \div 8 =$ .....   b $4.5 \div 9 =$ .....   c $3.6 \div 4 =$ .....

d $0.5 \times 3 =$ .....   e $0.6 \times 4 =$ .....   f $5 \times 0.4 =$ .....

g $1.2 \times 3 =$ .....   h $2.5 \times 3 =$ .....   i $1.2 \div 3 =$ .....

4 Use a calculator to check what happens when you multiply decimals by 10 or 100.

a $7.6 \times 10 =$ .....   b $8.3 \times 10 =$ .....   c $45.6 \times 10 =$ .....

d $36.7 \times 10 =$ .....   e $3.5 \times 100 =$ .....   f $6.8 \times 100 =$ .....

g $37.4 \times 100 =$ .....   h $74.6 \times 100 =$ .....   i $2.59 \times 100 =$ .....

Remember this
Multiplying by 10 moves each digit one place to the left; multiplying by 100 moves each digit two places to the left.

5 Look at the answers in question 4 to work out these calculations without a calculator.

a $3.2 \times 10 =$ .....   b $6.9 \times 10 =$ .....   c $57.5 \times 10 =$ .....

d $5.7 \times 100 =$ .....   e $8.2 \times 100 =$ .....   f $52.8 \times 100 =$ .....

g $34.8 \times 100 =$ .....   h $3.48 \times 100 =$ .....   i $7.89 \times 100 =$ .....

6 Use a calculator to check what happens when you divide whole numbers and decimals by 10 or 100.

    a 36 ÷ 10 = ...   **b** 72 ÷ 10 = ...   **c** 15.4 ÷ 10 = ...

    d 28.3 ÷ 10 = ...   **e** 5.6 ÷ 10 = ...   **f** 4.8 ÷ 10 = ...

    g 27 ÷ 100 = ...   **h** 93 ÷ 100 = ...   **i** 123 ÷ 100 = ...

    j 456 ÷ 100 = ...   **k** 6789 ÷ 100 = ...   **l** 5432 ÷ 100 = ...

7 Look at the answers in question 6 to work out these calculations without a calculator.

    a 49 ÷ 10 = ...   **b** 84 ÷ 10 = ...   **c** 17.6 ÷ 10 = ...

    d 37.4 ÷ 10 = ...   **e** 4.8 ÷ 10 = ...   **f** 8.9 ÷ 10 = ...

    g 36 ÷ 100 = ...   **h** 72 ÷ 100 = ...   **i** 468 ÷ 100 = ...

    j 752 ÷ 100 = ...   **k** 3764 ÷ 100 = ...   **l** 4821 ÷ 100 = ...

> **Remember this**
>
> Dividing by 10 moves each digit one place to the right; dividing by 100 moves each digit two places to the right.

8 Use a calculator to find which answer belongs to which calculation.

    a 17.08 × 6 = ...

    b 567.25 ÷ 5 = ...

    c 443.1 ÷ 4.2 = ...

    d 9.23 × 12.06 = ...

> 113.45   102.48
>
> 111.3138   105.5

Step into GCSE

9 a Use the fact that 24 × 8 = 192 to work out 2.4 × 8 = ...

    b Use the fact that 192 ÷ 8 = 24 to work out 19.2 ÷ 8 = ...

    c Work out the answers.

       1200 ÷ 1000 = ...   1.234 × 1000 = ...   3.2 × 6 = ...

Needs more practice ☐   Almost there ☐   I'm proficient! ☐

Rounding decimals

2.4

By the end of this section you will know how to:

✳ Round decimals to the nearest whole number

✳ Round decimals to one decimal place

> **GCSE LINKS**
>
> AF: 5.7 Rounding decimals;
> BF: Unit 2 3.7 Rounding decimals; 16+: 1.4 Rounding decimals

> **You should know**
>
> 5 and above round up,
> 4 and below round down.

Key points

✳ The same rules of rounding apply to decimals and whole numbers.

✳ Round to the nearest whole number: round 0.1, 0.2, 0.3 and 0.4 down; round 0.5, 0.6, 0.7, 0.8 and 0.9 up.

✳ Round to the one decimal place: round down if the hundredths digit is 1, 2, 3 or 4; round up if it is 5, 6, 7, 8 or 9.

Practice

1 Use the number line to help you to round these numbers to the nearest whole number.

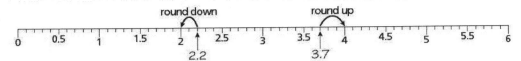

a 5.2 rounds to ....

b 5.8 rounds to ....

c 2.7 rounds to ....

d 3.4 rounds to ....

e 1.3 rounds to ....

f 4.5 rounds to ....

2 a Join each decimal to the nearest one decimal place. Use the number line to help.

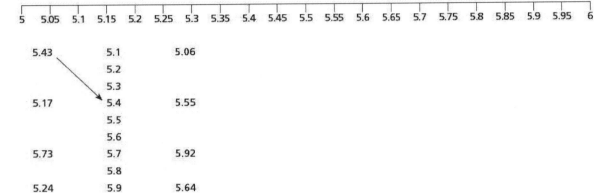

5.43   5.1   5.06

            5.2

            5.3

5.17   5.4   5.55

            5.5

            5.6

5.73   5.7   5.92

            5.8

5.24   5.9   5.64

b Write each number correct to the nearest whole number.

45.62 ....   45.263 ....   45.3456 ....

c Write each number correct to one decimal place.

45.62 ....   45.263 ....   45.3456 ....

> **Remember this**
>
> To round to the nearest whole number, look at the digit in the first decimal place. To round to one decimal place, look at the digit in the second decimal place.

Step into GCSE

3 a Write two decimal numbers that round up to 8. ....

b Write two decimal numbers that round down to 8. ....

c Write two decimal numbers that round up to 3.4 ....

d Write two decimal numbers that round down to 3.4 ....

e Write these decimals correct to one decimal place. 2.916 .... 3.672 .... 4.835 ....

f A number rounds up to 6, but down to 5.5. What number could it be? ....

Don't forget!

✳ When you multiply a number by 10, each digit moves one place to the ....

✳ When you divide a number by 100, each digit moves .... to the ....

✳ What is wrong with this?

$$
\begin{array}{r}
3\ 4\ .\ 5 \\
+\ 2\ .\ 5 \\
\hline
5\ 9\ .\ 5
\end{array}
$$

....

....

Exam-style questions

1 What is the value of the 6 in each of these numbers?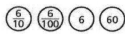

   a 34.67 ....   b 36.47 ....   c 34.76 ....

2 Write these numbers in order of size. Start with the smallest number.

   34.7   34.67   36.47   34.76   36.04

   ....

3 Round these numbers to the nearest whole number.

   a 24.67 ....   b 16.48 ....   c 29.706 ....

4 Round these numbers correct to one decimal place.

   a 15.33 ....   b 36.47 ....   c 41.062 ....

5 a Work out   56.4 + 31.78   b Work out   65.4 − 31.78

                    ....

6 Work out

   a 0.5 × 7 = ...   b 5 × 0.7 = ...   c 3.5 ÷ 7 = ...

   d 2.4 × 2 = ...   e 4.2 ÷ 7 = ...   f 4.6 × 4 = ...

7 Use your calculator to work out

   a 17.09 × 4.2   b 67.48 ÷ 12.05

                    ....

8 a Work out

      24.05 × 10 = ...   2460 ÷ 10 = ...

      23 900 ÷ 100 = ...   2.45 × 100 = ...

   b Write your answers to part a in order. Start with the smallest number.

   ....

Needs more practice ☐   Almost there ☐   I'm proficient! ☐

3.1 Check solutions

By the end of this section you will know how to:
* Check calculations with an inverse operation
* Check calculations using approximation

GCSE LINKS
AF: 5.10 Estimating;
BF: Unit 2 3.10 Decimals and rounding; 16+: 1.5 Estimating, 1.6 Checking calculations

Key points

* Use rounding to work out an approximate answer.
* Use inverse calculations and rounding to check answers.

> **You should know**
> Addition and subtraction are inverse operations. Multiplication and division are also inverse operations.

Guided

1 Write an inverse calculation to check these answers.

a $3 \times 4 = 12$ $12 \div 3 = $ ....

b $4 \times 9 = 36$ $36 \div $ .... $ = $ ....

c $24 \div 3 = 8$ .... $\times$ .... $=$ ....

d $54 \div 9 = 6$ .... $\times$ .... $=$ ....

e $34 + 56 = 90$ $90 - $ .... $=$ ....

f $100 - 56 = $ .... $56 + $ .... $=$ ....

2 Work out an approximate answer, using rounding to the nearest 10, 100 or 1. Then use a calculator to work out the actual answer. How close is your approximate answer?

a $48 + 52$ is about $50 + 50 = $ .... $48 + 52 = $ ....

b $121 - 59$ $120 - $ .... $=$ .... $121 - 59 = $ ....

c $618 - 498$ .... $-$ .... $=$ .... $618 - 498 = $ ....

d 43×59 .... $\times$ .... $=$ .... $43 \times 59 = $ ....

e 4.8×3.9 $5 \times $ .... $=$ .... $4.8 \times 3.9 = $ ....

f $25.6 \div 3.2$ .... $\div$ .... $=$ .... $25.6 \div 3.2 = $ ....

g $3.2 + 5.8 + 6.7$ .... $+$ .... $+$ .... $=$ .... $3.2 + 5.8 + 6.7 = $ ....

Practice

3 Use rounding to work out an approximate answer. Use this to choose the correct answer to these word problems from the numbers in the box.

| 51 | 82 | 216 | 270 | 494 |

a Eggs are packed in trays of 18. How many eggs are in 12 trays?   ....

b £357 is shared equally between seven people. How much does each receive?   £ ....

c Two friends are sharing a prize of £988. How much do they each get?   £ ....

d There are 15 players in a rugby team. How many players are needed for 18 teams?   ....

e Queen Victoria was born in 1819 and died in 1901. How many years is this?   ....

Step into GCSE

4 a Estimate the answers.

$6.9 \times 3.3 \longrightarrow$ .... $45.4 \div 8.7 \longrightarrow$ ....

b A pair of trainers costs £59.95. Estimate the cost of 4 pairs of trainers.

£ ....

c Eight boxes of printer paper cost £75. Estimate the cost of one box of printer paper.

£ ....

5 Dave has calculated that the total of 14.56 and 23.7 is 38.26

Choose the calculation you could use to check his answer.

☐ 23.7 − 38.26 ☐ 38.26 − 23.7 ☐ 38.26 + 14.56 ☐ 23.7 − 14.56

Don't forget!

✳ To work out an approximate answer you need to ....

✳ To check an answer you can use .... or use ....

✳ Addition and .... are inverse operations.

✳ Write two facts related to $5 \times 6 = 30$. .... and ....

Exam-style questions

1 Use rounding to work out an approximate answer to 21.09×3.9 .... × .... = ...

2 Use rounding to help to match the calculation to its approximate answer.

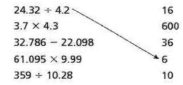

24.32 ÷ 4.2   16
3.7 × 4.3   600
32.786 − 22.098 36
61.095 × 9.99   6
359 ÷ 10.28   10

3 a Five pairs of socks cost £19.50. Estimate the cost of one pair of socks.

£ ....

b One roll of ribbon costs £10.15. Estimate the cost of 8 rolls of ribbon.

£ ....

4 Write a calculation you could use to check each answer.

a $23.37 + 45.08 = 68.45$ ....

b $34.4 \times 21.5 = 739.6$ ....

c $12.88 \div 5.6 = 2.3$ ....

4.1 Read, write and order fractions

By the end of this section you will know how to:

* Read, write, order and compare fractions and mixed numbers

Remember this

A mixed number is the same as a mixed fraction — it is a whole number with a fractional part, e.g. $3\frac{1}{2}$

GCSE LINKS

AF: 8.1 Understanding fractions, 8.3 Ordering fractions; BF: Unit 2 4.1 Understanding fractions, 4.3 Ordering fractions; 16+: 2.1 Ordering and converting fractions

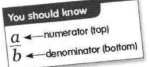

Key points

* As the denominator increases, the fractional part gets smaller.
* A fraction is part of a whole one.

You should know

$\dfrac{a}{b}$ ← numerator (top)

← denominator (bottom)

Guided

1 Write the fraction that is shaded and the fraction that is **not** shaded.

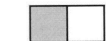

a $\frac{1}{2}$ shaded $\frac{1}{2}$ not shaded   b $\frac{\ }{4}$ shaded   .... not shaded

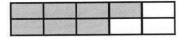

c   .... shaded   .... not shaded   d   .... shaded   .... not shaded

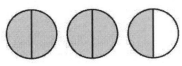

e $1\frac{1}{4}$ shaded   .... not shaded   f   .... shaded   .... not shaded

Practice

2 Shade the shapes to show these fractions.

a $\frac{1}{5}$ b $\frac{1}{3}$ c $\frac{1}{2}$ d $\frac{1}{4}$ e $\frac{1}{10}$

3 Use the shaded shapes in question 2 to write these fractions in order, starting with the smallest.

$$\frac{1}{5} \quad \frac{1}{3} \quad \frac{1}{2} \quad \frac{1}{4} \quad \frac{1}{10}$$

....

4 Shade the shapes to show these fractions. Then write them in order from smallest to largest.

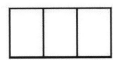
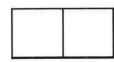

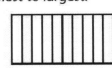

a $\frac{4}{5}$ b $\frac{2}{3}$ c $\frac{1}{2}$ d $\frac{3}{4}$ e $\frac{9}{10}$

Step into GCSE

5 Using what you learned in questions 2 and 4, write these fractions in order. Start with the smallest.

a $\frac{1}{3}$ $\frac{1}{7}$ $\frac{1}{5}$ $\frac{1}{2}$ $\frac{1}{4}$ $\frac{1}{6}$ ....

b $\frac{9}{10}$ $\frac{5}{6}$ $\frac{11}{12}$ $\frac{2}{3}$ $\frac{7}{8}$ $\frac{4}{5}$ ....

6 Continue the pattern of fractions. Write the next three numbers in each pattern.

a $\frac{1}{2}$ 1 $1\frac{1}{2}$ 2 $2\frac{1}{2}$ 3 ....

b $\frac{1}{4}$ $\frac{2}{4}$ $\frac{3}{4}$ 1 $1\frac{1}{4}$ $1\frac{2}{4}$ ....

c $\frac{1}{2}$ $\frac{1}{3}$ $\frac{1}{4}$ $\frac{1}{5}$ ....

d $\frac{1}{2}$ $\frac{2}{3}$ $\frac{3}{4}$ $\frac{4}{5}$ ....

Needs more practice ☐   Almost there ☐   I'm proficient! ☐

4.2 Use equivalent fractions

By the end of this section you will know how to:
* Identify equivalent fractions

GCSE LINKS
AF: 8.2 Equivalent fractions;
BF: Unit 2 4.2 Equivalent fractions

Key points

* **Equivalent** means equal.
* Any fraction has many equivalent fractions.

Guided

1 These pairs of fractions are equivalent. Write the equivalent fractions.

a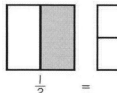

$\frac{1}{2} = \frac{2}{.....}$

b

$\frac{3}{4} = \frac{.....}{.....}$

c

$............. = ...$

d

$............. = ...$

Practice

2 Use the fraction board to identify some more equivalent fractions.

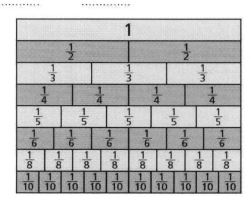

a $\frac{1}{2} = \frac{.....}{4} = \frac{.....}{6} = \frac{.....}{10}$ b $\frac{1}{3} = \frac{.....}{6}$ c $\frac{2}{5} = \frac{.....}{10}$

d $\frac{3}{4} = \frac{.....}{8}$ e $\frac{2}{3} = \frac{.....}{6}$ f $\frac{8}{10} = \frac{.....}{5}$

g $\frac{2}{6} = \frac{1}{.....}$ h $\frac{6}{10} = \frac{3}{.....}$ i $\frac{2}{4} = \frac{4}{.....}$

3 Complete these sets of equivalent fractions.

Guided

a $\dfrac{1}{2} \overset{\times 2}{\underset{\times 2}{=}} \dfrac{2}{4} \overset{\times 2}{\underset{\times 2 \ \dots}{=}} \dfrac{4}{\dots} \overset{\times 2}{\underset{\times 2}{=}} \dfrac{\dots}{16}$

b $\dfrac{2}{3} \overset{\times 10}{\underset{\times 10 \ \dots}{=}} \dfrac{20}{\dots}$

c $\dfrac{3}{10} \overset{\times 3}{\underset{\times 3 \ \dots}{=}} \dfrac{\dots}{\dots}$

> **Remember this**
> You can make equivalent fractions by multiplying both parts of a fraction by the same number.

4 Write equivalent fractions for these fractions.

Practice

a $\dfrac{3}{4} = \dfrac{\dots}{\dots} = \dfrac{\dots}{\dots}$

b $\dfrac{5}{8} = \dfrac{\dots}{\dots} = \dfrac{\dots}{\dots}$

c $\dfrac{4}{5} = \dfrac{\dots}{\dots} = \dfrac{\dots}{\dots}$

Needs more practice ☐   Almost there ☐   I'm proficient! ☐

4.3 Write fractions in their simplest form

> **GCSE LINKS**
> AF: 8.2 Equivalent fractions;
> BF: Unit 2 4.2 Equivalent fractions; 16+: 2.1 Order fractions

By the end of this section you will know how to:

✳ Simplify (cancel down) fractions

> **You should know**
> The factors of a number have that number in their times tables.

Key points

✳ **Simplifying** is the opposite of finding equivalent fractions by multiplying.

✳ Fractions are **simplified** by dividing the numerator and the denominator by the same number.

✳ A fraction is in its **simplest form** when you can't divide the numerator and denominator any further.

1 Write these fractions as simply as possible.

Guided

a

$\dfrac{2}{8} = \dfrac{1}{\dots}$

b

$\dfrac{6}{10} = \dfrac{\dots}{\dots}$

c

$\dfrac{\dots}{\dots} = \dfrac{\dots}{\dots}$

d

$\dfrac{\dots}{\dots} = \dfrac{\dots}{\dots}$

e

$\dfrac{\dots}{\dots} = \dfrac{\dots}{\dots}$

f

$\dfrac{\dots}{\dots} = \dfrac{\dots}{\dots}$

2 Simplify these fractions.

Practice

a $\dfrac{5}{10} \overset{\div 5}{\underset{\div 5 \ \dots}{=}} \dfrac{\dots}{\dots}$

b $\dfrac{14}{20} \overset{\div 2}{\underset{\div 2 \ \dots}{=}} \dfrac{\dots}{\dots}$

c $\dfrac{12}{15} \overset{\div 3}{\underset{\div 3 \ \dots}{=}} \dfrac{\dots}{\dots}$

d $\dfrac{6}{12} = \dfrac{\dots}{\dots}$

e $\dfrac{15}{20} = \dfrac{\dots}{\dots}$

f $\dfrac{12}{16} = \dfrac{\dots}{\dots}$

> **Remember this**
> Simplify fractions by dividing both parts of the fraction by the same number.

Step into GCSE

3 Join the pairs of equivalent fractions

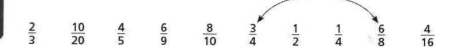

$\frac{2}{3}$ $\frac{10}{20}$ $\frac{4}{5}$ $\frac{6}{9}$ $\frac{8}{10}$ $\frac{3}{4}$ $\frac{1}{2}$ $\frac{1}{4}$ $\frac{6}{8}$ $\frac{4}{16}$

Needs more practice ☐   Almost there ☐   I'm proficient! ☐

4.4 Convert between fractions and decimals

GCSE LINKS
AF: 8.8 Fractions and decimals;
BF: Unit 2 4.8 Fractions and decimals

By the end of this section you will know how to:

* Convert simple fractions to decimals
* Convert simple decimals to fractions

Key points

* All fractions have a decimal equivalent.
* All decimals have a fraction equivalent.

Guided

1 a Choose the decimals and fractions from this box to complete the two number lines.

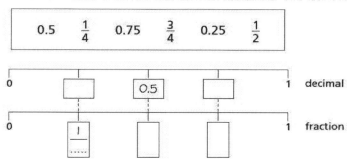

0.5 $\frac{1}{4}$ 0.75 $\frac{3}{4}$ 0.25 $\frac{1}{2}$

b Use the number lines to find the pairs of equivalent fractions and decimals.

$\frac{1}{4} = 0.\ldots$ $\frac{1}{2} = \ldots$ $\frac{\ldots}{\ldots} = \ldots$

Practice

2 a Complete both number lines.

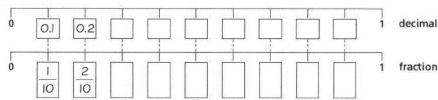

b Use the completed number lines to write the equivalent fractions and decimals.

$0.1 = \frac{\ldots}{\ldots}$ $\frac{2}{10} = \ldots$ $0.4 = \frac{\ldots}{\ldots}$ $\frac{9}{10} = \ldots$

Guided

3 Use a calculator to change these fractions into decimals.

    a $\frac{1}{5} = 1 \div 5 = 0.\underline{\dots\dots}$ **b** $\frac{3}{5} = 3 \div 5 = \underline{\dots\dots}$ **c** $\frac{4}{5} = \underline{\dots\dots} \div \underline{\dots\dots} = \underline{\dots\dots}$

    d $\frac{1}{20} = \underline{\dots\dots} \div \underline{\dots\dots} = \underline{\dots\dots}$ **e** $\frac{3}{20} = \underline{\dots\dots\dots\dots\dots}$ **f** $\frac{21}{25} = \underline{\dots\dots\dots\dots\dots}$

Step into GCSE

4 Convert the fractions into decimals. Then write them in order, starting with the smallest.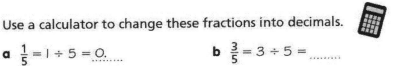

Fraction	$\frac{3}{4}$	$\frac{2}{5}$	$\frac{5}{8}$	$\frac{12}{15}$	$\frac{9}{20}$
Decimal					

Order ....

Convert decimals into fractions

Remember this

0.5 means 5 tenths $= \frac{5}{10}$

0.45 means 45 hundredths $= \frac{45}{100}$

Guided

5 Change these decimals into a fraction in tenths or hundredths. Then simplify where possible.

    a $0.8 = \frac{8}{10} \overset{\div 2}{\underset{\div 2 \ \dots}{}} = \underline{\dots\dots}$ **b** $0.7 = \frac{\dots\dots}{\dots\dots}$ **c** $0.4 = \frac{\dots\dots}{\dots\dots} = \frac{\dots\dots}{\dots\dots}$

    d $0.15 = \frac{15}{100} \overset{\div 5}{\underset{\div 5 \ \dots}{}} = \underline{\dots\dots}$ **e** $0.19 = \frac{\dots\dots}{\dots\dots}$ **f** $0.28 = \frac{\dots\dots}{\dots\dots} \overset{\div 4}{\underset{\div 4}{}} = \frac{\dots\dots}{\dots\dots}$

Step into GCSE

6 Complete the table to show the equivalent fractions and decimals.

Decimal	0.5		0.9		0.2	
Fraction		$\frac{3}{4}$		$\frac{11}{100}$		$\frac{3}{10}$

Needs more practice ☐   Almost there ☐   I'm proficient! ☐

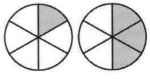

Add and subtract fractions

By the end of this section you will know how to:

  ✳ Add and subtract fractions with the same denominator

GCSE LINKS

AF: 8.7 Adding and subtracting fractions; BF: Unit 2 4.7 Adding and subtracting fractions; 16+: 2.2 Adding and subtracting fractions

Key points

  ✳ Fractions with the same denominator can be added and subtracted easily.

You should know

How to read a shaded diagram showing a fraction.

Guided

1 Show these fraction diagrams as an addition.

    a 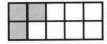   **b** 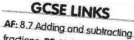   **c**

    $\frac{1}{6} + \frac{3}{6} = \frac{\dots}{6}$ $\frac{3}{10} + \frac{\dots\dots}{\dots\dots} = \frac{\dots\dots}{\dots\dots}$ $\frac{\dots\dots}{\dots\dots} + \frac{\dots\dots}{\dots\dots} = \frac{\dots\dots}{\dots\dots}$

Practice

2 Add these fractions. Simplify your answers where possible.

a $\frac{1}{5} + \frac{3}{5} = \underline{\quad}$

b $\frac{5}{10} + \frac{3}{10} = \underline{\quad} = \underline{\quad}$

c $\frac{1}{8} + \frac{5}{8} = \underline{\quad} = \underline{\quad}$

3 Subtract these fractions. Simplify your answers where possible.

a $\frac{4}{5} - \frac{1}{5} = \underline{\quad}$

b $\frac{7}{10} - \frac{2}{10} = \underline{\quad} = \underline{\quad}$

c $\frac{5}{6} - \frac{2}{6} = \underline{\quad} = \underline{\quad}$

d $\frac{7}{9} - \frac{3}{9} = \underline{\quad}$

Step into GCSE

4 Work out the answers. Write the fraction in its simplest form.

a $\frac{7}{12} + \frac{3}{12} = \underline{\quad}$

b $\frac{7}{12} - \frac{3}{12} = \underline{\quad}$

c $\frac{4}{9} + \frac{4}{9} = \underline{\quad}$

d $\frac{6}{11} - \frac{5}{11} = \underline{\quad}$

Needs more practice ☐   Almost there ☐   I'm proficient! ☐

4.6 Find fractions of quantities

By the end of this section you will know how to:

✳ Find a fraction of a quantity

✳ Multiply a fraction by a positive integer

GCSE LINKS

AF: 8.5 Multiplying fractions;
BF: Unit 2 4.5 Multiplying fractions; 16+: 2.3, 2.5 Multiplying and dividing fractions

Key points

✳ To multiply a fraction, multiply the numerator.

✳ To find a fraction of a number, divide by the denominator.

Remember this

A fraction is a way of showing division, e.g. $\frac{3}{10} = 3 \div 10$.

Guided

1 Write these as multiplications to find the answer.

a

b

c

You should know

Related division facts for 2, 3, 4, 5 and 10 times tables.

a $2 \times \frac{1}{3} = \frac{\underline{\quad}}{3}$

b $3 \times \frac{\underline{\quad}}{10} = \frac{\underline{\quad}}{\underline{\quad}} = \frac{\underline{\quad}}{\underline{\quad}}$

c $\underline{\quad} \times \frac{\underline{\quad}}{5} = \frac{\underline{\quad}}{\underline{\quad}}$

Practice

2 Work out these multiplications. Simplify where possible.

a $3 \times \frac{1}{8} = \underline{\quad}$

b $4 \times \frac{1}{7} = \underline{\quad}$

c $2 \times \frac{3}{10} = \underline{\quad}$

d $3 \times \frac{4}{20} = \underline{\quad}$

e $\frac{4}{15} \times 2 = \underline{\quad}$

f $\frac{2}{11} \times 5 = \underline{\quad}$

g $\frac{3}{7} \times 2 = \underline{\quad}$

h $5 \times \frac{3}{20} = \underline{\quad}$

i $\frac{2}{9} \times 3 = \underline{\quad}$

Guided

3 Find the fraction of the number using division.

a $\frac{1}{2}$ of 16 = 16 ÷ 2 = ...

b $\frac{1}{3}$ of 12 = 12 ÷ .... = ...

c $\frac{1}{5}$ of 20 = ... ÷ .... = ...

d $\frac{1}{4}$ of 20 = ... = ...

e $\frac{1}{10}$ of 20 = ... = ...

f $\frac{1}{3}$ of 18 = ... = ...

> **Remember this**
> To find $\frac{1}{2}$ divide by **2**;
> to find $\frac{1}{4}$ divide by **4**.

Practice

4 Find the fraction of the number using division.

a $\frac{1}{10}$ of 40 = ...

b $\frac{1}{5}$ of 25 = ...

c $\frac{1}{6}$ of 30 = ...

d $\frac{1}{9}$ of 27 = ...

e $\frac{1}{8}$ of 32 = ...

f $\frac{1}{7}$ of 28 = ...

Guided

5 **a** Find $\frac{1}{5}$ of these apples, by dividing them into the five crates.

b Find these fractions.

$\frac{1}{5}$ of 30 = 30 ÷ .... = ...

$\frac{2}{5}$ of 30 = $\frac{1}{5}$ of 30 × 2 = 30 ÷ 5 × 2 = ... × 2 = ...

$\frac{3}{5}$ of 30 = ... × 3 = ...

$\frac{4}{5}$ of 30 = ... × .... = ...

> **Hint**
> To find $\frac{3}{5}$ of a number,
> find $\frac{1}{5}$ by dividing by **5**,
> then multiply by **3** to
> find $\frac{3}{5}$.

Practice

6 Use division then multiplication to find these fractions.

a $\frac{3}{4}$ of 20 = ...

b $\frac{7}{10}$ of 40 = ...

c $\frac{4}{5}$ of 50 = ...

d $\frac{3}{8}$ of 24 = ...

e $\frac{3}{10}$ of 60 = ...

f $\frac{2}{3}$ of 30 = ...

Step into GCSE

7 Work out the answers.

a $\frac{3}{4}$ of 60 = ...

b $\frac{3}{5}$ of 150 = ...

c $\frac{5}{6}$ of 120 = ...

d $\frac{9}{10}$ of 450 = ...

e $\frac{4}{11}$ of 66 = ...

f $\frac{4}{9}$ of 72 = ...

Don't forget!

⁎ Shade each shape to show the fraction.

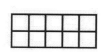

a $\frac{3}{5}$ **b** $\frac{5}{6}$ **c** $\frac{3}{10}$

⁎ Match the equivalent fractions.

$\frac{3}{4}$ $\frac{2}{3}$ $\frac{1}{2}$ $\frac{1}{4}$

$\frac{15}{30}$ $\frac{15}{20}$ $\frac{5}{20}$ $\frac{20}{30}$

⁎ Fill in the table of equivalent fractions and decimals.

Decimal		0.5		0.01		0.17
Fraction	$\frac{1}{10}$		$\frac{9}{10}$		$\frac{4}{100}$	

⁎ To change a decimal into a fraction you ....,

then .... the fraction if you can.

⁎ To find $\frac{1}{5}$ of a quantity you ....

⁎ To find $\frac{3}{4}$ of a quantity you .... then ....

Exam-style questions

1 a Work out $\frac{3}{7} + \frac{2}{7}$ .... **b** Work out $\frac{7}{8} - \frac{5}{8}$ ....

2 a Work out $\frac{1}{5}$ of 35 .... **b** Work out $\frac{1}{4}$ of 24 ....

3 a Work out $\frac{3}{4}$ of 32 .... **b** Work out $\frac{3}{10}$ of 40 ....

4 a Find an equivalent fraction to $\frac{10}{20}$ .... **b** Write $\frac{8}{10}$ in its simplest form. ....

5 a Write 0.7 as a fraction. .... **b** Write $\frac{1}{4}$ as a decimal. ....

6 Work out $\frac{1}{4}$ of £40.   £ ....

7 Write these fractions in order of size. Start with the smallest fraction.

$\frac{1}{4}$ $\frac{3}{4}$ $\frac{1}{2}$ $\frac{1}{5}$ ....

5.1 Decimals, fractions and percentages

GCSE LINKS
AF: 19.1 Conversion and equivalence; BF: Unit 2 5.1 Conversion and equivalence

By the end of this section you will know how to:

✶ Convert some decimals and fractions into percentages

✶ Convert percentages into decimals and fractions

Key points

✶ Percentage means out of 100.

✶ 100% means $\frac{100}{100}$, all, the whole, everything.

✶ All percentages have a decimal and a fraction equivalent.

Practice

1 Colour the grids to show the percentages.

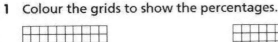

a 50%   b 85%   c 23%

Guided

2 Complete these number lines.

a

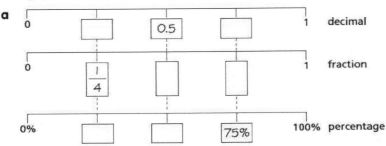

> **You should know**
> The decimal equivalents for quarters and tenths.
> The fraction equivalents for 0.25, 0.5, 0.75 and all tenths.

b

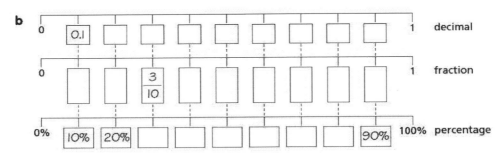

Practice

3 Use the number lines to complete these equivalent fractions, decimals and percentages.

a $0.5 = \text{.........} \% = \frac{\text{.....}}{\text{.....}}$ b $25\% = \frac{\text{.....}}{\text{.....}} = \text{.........}$ c $\frac{3}{4} = \text{.........} \% = \text{.........}$

d $0.1 = \text{.........} \% = \frac{\text{.....}}{\text{.....}}$ e $20\% = \frac{\text{.....}}{\text{.....}} = \text{.........}$ f $\frac{7}{10} = \text{.........} \% = \text{.........}$

Step into GCSE

4 Complete the table to show the equivalent decimals, fractions and percentages.

Fraction	Decimal	Percentage
$\frac{3}{10}$		
	0.25	
		90%
$\frac{4}{10}$		
	0.8	
		75%

Guided

5 Convert each fraction into an equivalent decimal, then write the equivalent percentage.

    Divide fraction (decimal)   × 100 (percentage)

a $\frac{1}{5} = 1 \div 5 = 0.2$ $0.2 \times 100 =$ .... %

b $\frac{3}{5} = 3 \div 5 =$ .... $\times 100 =$ .... %

c $\frac{1}{20} =$ .... $=$ .... $\times$ .... $=$ .... %

6 Convert each percentage into a decimal by dividing by 100.

a $45\% \overset{\div 100}{=} 0.$ .....   **b** $40\% = 0.$ .....   **c** $4\% = 0.$ .....

> **You should know**
> How to divide a 2-digit number by 100.

7 Convert each percentage into a fraction, simplifying where you can.

a $20\% = \frac{20}{100} \overset{\div 10}{\underset{\div 10}{=}} \frac{2}{10} \overset{\div 2}{\underset{\div 2}{=}} \frac{.....}{.....}$ **b** $11\% = \frac{.....}{100}$ **c** $9\% = \frac{9}{.....}$

Practice

8 a Convert these fractions into percentages.

$\frac{11}{20} =$ .... $\frac{15}{20} =$ ....

$\frac{1}{8} =$ .... $\frac{3}{8} =$ ....

b Convert these percentages into decimals.

$35\% =$ .... $80\% =$ .... $8\% =$ ....

$15\% =$ .... $30\% =$ .... $9\% =$ ....

c Convert these percentages into fractions, simplifying where possible.

$30\% =$ .... $29\% =$ .... $3\% =$ ....

$35\% =$ .... $80\% =$ .... $22\% =$ ....

Step into GCSE

9 Find the sets of three equivalents – a decimal, a fraction and percentage. Record them in the table.

0.7   40% $\frac{7}{10}$ 0.17

0.75   50% $\frac{15}{20}$ 0.5

$\frac{2}{5}$ 75%   0.4 $\frac{20}{40}$

$\frac{17}{100}$ 70%   17%

Fraction	Decimal	Percentage

Needs more practice ☐   Almost there ☐   I'm proficient! ☐

5.2 Order and compare percentages

By the end of this section you will know how to:
- ∗ Order and compare percentages of amounts
- ∗ Use the equivalence of fractions, decimals and percentages

GCSE LINKS
AF: 19.1 Conversion and equivalence, 19.2 Percentages;
BF: Unit 2 5.1 Conversion and equivalence, 5.2 Percentages;
Unit 3 2.1, 2.2 Percentages

Key points

∗ Equivalence can be used to order fractions, decimals and percentages.

Guided

1 Change the fractions and decimals into percentages to order them. Start with the smallest.

a 0.35   25% $\frac{3}{10}$

    35%   25%   30%

    25% $\frac{3}{10}$ ....

b 0.89 $\frac{9}{10}$ 87%

    89%   ....%   ....

    87%   ....

c $\frac{3}{5}$ 0.59   63%

    60 ....

    ....

Practice

2 Write these fractions, decimals and percentages in order. Start with the smallest.

You should know
$\frac{21}{25} = \frac{42}{50} = \frac{84}{100} = 84\%$.
$\frac{12}{20} = 12 \div 20 = 0.6 = 60\%$.

a 0.7 $\frac{3}{4}$ 74%   ....

b $\frac{1}{5}$ 21%   0.19   ....

c 0.72   65% $\frac{7}{10}$ ....

d 0.81   78% $\frac{4}{5}$ ....

e $\frac{1}{10}$ 0.12   9%   ....

f 17%   0.2 $\frac{3}{20}$ ....

g 0.5 $\frac{11}{20}$ 53%   ....

h $\frac{5}{8}$ 49%   0.6   ....

i $\frac{21}{25}$ 0.85   83%   ....

Step into GCSE

3 a Change these scores into percentages using a calculator or by changing the fractions to hundredths.

Maths $\frac{77}{100}$ $\frac{77}{100}$ = ...%

English $\frac{36}{50}$ $\frac{36}{50}$ = $\frac{}{100}$ = ...%

Science $\frac{21}{25}$ $\frac{21}{25}$ = $\frac{}{50}$ = $\frac{}{100}$ = ...%

Art $\frac{7}{10}$ $\frac{7}{10}$ = $\frac{}{100}$ = ...%

RE $\frac{16}{20}$ $\frac{16}{20}$ = $\frac{}{10}$ = $\frac{}{100}$ = ...%

b Write the subjects in order, starting with the best test score.

....

Needs more practice ☐   Almost there ☐   I'm proficient! ☐

Find percentages of quantities

5.3

By the end of this section you will know how to:

✱ Find 10%, 20%, 5% and 15% of a quantity mentally and with a calculator

✱ Find 25%, 50% and 75% of a quantity mentally and with a calculator

✱ Work out VAT payable

✱ Order percentages of quantities

GCSE LINKS

AF: 19.2, 19.3 Percentages;

BF: Unit 2 5.2 Percentages,

Unit 3 2.1, 2.2 Percentages;

16+: 4.1 Percentages

Key points

✱ 10% = $\frac{1}{10}$

✱ 5% is half of 10%.

✱ A 2-digit percentage of a number is always less than the number.

✱ 20% is double 10%.

✱ 15% is 10% + 5%.

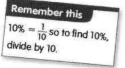

Remember this

10% = $\frac{1}{10}$ so to find 10%, divide by 10.

Find 10%, 20%, 5% and 15% of quantities

You should know

How to divide any number by 10.

Guided

1 Find 10% of these amounts by dividing by 10.

a 10% of £300 = 300 ÷ 10 = £ ....

b 10% of £65 = 65 ÷ 10 = ... = £6.50

c 10% of £124 = ... ÷ ...... = 12. ..... = £ ....

d 10% of £388 = ...

Practice

2 Find 10% of these amounts – remember to write the unit of measure.

a 10% of £60 = ...

b 10% of £56 = ...

c 10% of £286 = ...

d 10% of 620 g = ...

e 10% of 3400 ml = ...

f 10% of 450 cm = ...

g 10% of 700 km = ...

h 10% of 3500 g = ...

i 10% of £4000 = ...

Guided

3 Find 20% by doubling 10% and find 5% by halving 10%.

   a 20% of £30 = (10% of 30) × 2 = 3 × 2 = ...   20% of £30 = £ ....

   b 5% of £400 = (10% of 400) ÷ 2 = 40 ÷ 2 = ...   5% of £400 = £ ....

   c 20% of £75 = (10% of 75) × 2 = ...   20% of £75 = £ ....

   d 5% of £60 = (10% of ....) ÷ .... = ...   5% of £60 = £ ....

   e 20% of £140 = ...   20% of £140 = £ ....

   f 5% of £120 = ...   5% of £120 = £ ....

Practice

4 Find 15% by finding 10% and 5% and adding.

Amount	10%	5%	10% + 5%	15% of amount
£60				15% of £60 =
£100				15% of £100 =
£120				15% of £120 =
£360				15% of £360 =
£240				15% of £240 =
£500				15% of £500 =

5 Work out these percentages.

  a 10% of £45   **b** 20% of £50   **c** 5% of £160

  d 15% of £80   **e** 10% of £15   **f** 20% of £70

  g 5% of £440   **h** 15% of £320   **i** 20% of £150

  j 10% of £648   **k** 20% of £420   **l** 15% of £1000

6 Work out which pairs of percentages have the same answer. Then complete the statements.

| 50% of £50 | 25% of £120 | 10% of £300 | 20% of £100 | 10% of £250 | 5% of £400 |

50% of £50 = ... = ...

.... = ... = ...

.... = ... = ...

Step into GCSE

7 Work out the answers.

a Work out 5% of £70.

b Work out 15% of £70.

c Work out 30% of £40.

....

....

....

d 54% of a school are boys. What percentage are girls? ....

e 10% of a number is 8. What is the number? ....

Find 25%, 50%, and 75% of quantities

Practice

8 a Write $\frac{1}{2}$ as a percentage. ....

b Write 25% as a fraction. ....

> **Remember this**
>
> To find 50%: divide by 2.
> To find 25%: divide by 4.
> 25% = 50% ÷ 2
> 75% = 50% + 25%

Guided

9 Work out these percentages

a 50% of £120 = 120 ÷ 2 = £ ....

b 25% of £120 = 120 ÷ 4 = £ ....

c 25% of £80 = 80 ÷ .... = £ ....

d 50% of £80 = ... ÷ .... = £ ....

e 75% of £120 = 50% of 120 + ... of 120 = ... + ... = £ ....

f 75% of £80 = ... + ... = ... + ... = £ ....

Practice

10 Work out these percentages of £180.

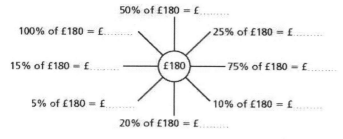

50% of £180 = £ ....
100% of £180 = £ ....
25% of £180 = £ ....
15% of £180 = £ .... — £180 — 75% of £180 = £ ....
5% of £180 = £ ....
10% of £180 = £ ....
20% of £180 = £ ....

Guided

11 Work out these percentages.

a 25% of 364 = 364 × 25 ÷ 100 = £ ....

b 75% of £440 = 440 × .... ÷ .... = £ ....

c 85% of £360 = ... × .... ÷ .... = £ ....

d 42% of £450 = ... × .... ÷ .... = £ ....

> **Remember this**
>
> To use a calculator to work out percentages, multiply the amount by the percentage then divide by 100.

Step into GCSE

12 a A dress costs £64. The price is reduced by 50%. What is the new price?

£ ....

b Which is better value? Show your working out.

£40

$\frac{2}{5}$ OFF

£40

25% reduction

....

13 Shade 25% of these diagrams.

a

b

c
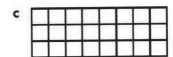

Remember this
Value added tax (VAT) is calculated as a percentage of the price.

Value added tax (VAT)

Guided

14 VAT of 20% is charged on these amounts. Find the amount of VAT charged.

a £50: 20% VAT = £50 ÷ 10 × 2 = £ ....

b £90: 20% VAT = £90 ÷ ...... × ...... = £ ....

c £45: 20% VAT = ... ÷ ...... × ...... = £ ....

d £75: 20% VAT = ...

Practice

15 Work out the tax on goods that cost these amounts.

a 15% tax on £50

b 25% tax on £60

c 10% tax on £75

....

....

....

d 20% tax on £35

e 20% tax on £125

f 15% tax on £150

....

....

....

16 Work out

Hint
2.5% is half of 5%.

a 10% of £80

b 5% of £80

c 2.5% of £80

....

....

....

d Use your answers to **a**, **b** and **c** to work out 17.5% of £80.

£ ....

Step into GCSE

17 A bill was £110 plus VAT at 20%. Complete the bill below.

Bill	
Cost of work	£110.00
+ VAT at 20%	£ ....
Total	£ ....

Don't forget!

✳ Match the statements that mean the same.

100% $\frac{1}{2}$ **price**   **save 25%**

| 50% off | | $\frac{1}{4}$ off | | the whole amount |

✳ To find 20% of an amount you find .... % of it then .... this.

Exam-style questions

1 a Write 0.9 as a percentage. ....   **b** Write 68% as a decimal. ....

   c Write 75% as a fraction. Write your answer in its simplest form.

....

2 a Write 0.72 as a percentage. ....   **b** Write 6% as a decimal. ....

3 Write these numbers in order of size. Start with the smallest number.

75%   0.7 $\frac{4}{5}$

....

4 a Work out   10% of £90 ....   **b** Work out   10% of £75 ....

5 a Work out   5% of £100 ....   **b** Work out   20% of £400 ....

6 Amy wants to buy a phone. The phone costs £180 plus VAT at 20%.
Work out the amount of VAT Amy pays.

£ ....

7 A bill was £45 plus VAT at 20%. Work out the VAT to be paid.

£ ....

8 Ali wants to buy a jacket. The cost of the jacket is £84. He pays a 25% deposit.
Work out 25% of £84.

£ ....

9 A café bill is £36.00. A tip of 10% is added.
Complete the bill to show the total cost
including the tip.

Café bill	
Lunch and drinks	£36.00
+ Tip at 10%	£ ....
Total	£ ....

6.1 Read and order amounts of money

By the end of this section you will know how to:
* Order and compare amounts of money
* Record amounts of money correctly

Key points

* There are 100 pence in one pound (£1).

* Amounts of money in pounds and pence are recorded as a whole number and a decimal part with two decimal places.

* When displaying an amount of money in pounds, a calculator display of 8.4 means £8.40, 0.3 means £0.30 or 30p, and 0.67 means £0.67 or 67p.

Guided

1 Count up the money in each purse, and record it correctly in pounds and pence.

Remember this
Write £6.50 or £6.05, never £6.5 or £6.50p.

a

£2 + £1 + 50p + 20p +10p + 5p

= £ ....

b

....

= £ ....

c

....

= £ ....

d

....

= £ ....

Practice

2 Write these items in order of their price. Start with the cheapest.

Cheese	£1.75
Apples	£1.30
Lettuce	90p
Eggs	£2.08
Cream	83p

....

....

....

....

....

3 Work out the total amounts of money.

a 3 × £7.50 = £ ....

b £2.25 × 8 = £ ....

c £3.75 × 16 = £ ....

d £20 ÷ 8 = £ ....

e £40.50 ÷ 10 = £ ....

f £750.60 ÷ 15 = £ ....

g £45.70 + £32.80 = £ ....

h £682.50 − £352.99 = £ ....

i £3.15 + 65p = £ ....

j £2.09 − 7p = £ ....

k The total of the amounts in **a** to **j** £ ....

> **Remember this**
>
> When calculating amounts of money in pounds, a calculator display of 4.5 means £4.50. 45p needs be entered as 0.45

Needs more practice ☐   Almost there ☐   I'm proficient! ☐

Calculating with money

6.2

By the end of this section you will know how to:

∗ Add, subtract, multiply and divide amounts of money with and without a calculator

∗ Work out bills, wages and budgets

∗ Work out simple interest and repayments, including rounding to the nearest penny

Key points

∗ Managing money is an essential life skill.

∗ Paying bills, tax, working out simple interest and being able to budget are important.

∗ You will use all the skills you have learned so far in this chapter.

Guided

1 Match up the prices with their change from £10.

£3.45	£5.15	£5.65	£9.05
£0.95	£4.50	£3.35	£7.65
£2.35	£1.25	£6.55	£4.85
£6.65	£4.35	£5.50	£8.75

£3.45 + £6.55 = £10   .... + ... = £10

.... + ... = £10   .... + ... = £10

.... + ... = £10   .... + ... = £10

.... + ... = £10   .... + ... = £10

Working out the cost

> **You should know**
>
> How to add, subtract, multiply and divide decimals.

Guided

2 Use the prices of the items on the list to work out the cost.

a 4 rolls of wallpaper   4 × £ .... = £ ....

b 1 pack of brushes and a packet of paste

£ .... + £0.85 = £ ....

c 2 litres of paint £ .... × .... = £ ....

d 3 rolls of wallpaper, a litre of paint and a pack of brushes

3 × £ .... + £ .... + £ .... = £ ....

Wallpaper	£10 a roll
Wallpaper paste	85p a packet
Brushes (5)	£2.50 a pack
Paint	£12.50 for 1 litre

Practice

3 a Work out the total cost of these items.

Bread	£1.20
Butter	95p
Cheese	£1.80
TOTAL	

b Write the correct coins to pay the bill with the **exact** money.

....

Step into GCSE

4 a Sasha buys a sandwich and cake. She pays with two £2 coins. How much change should she get?

Take Away Snack Menu	
Sandwich	£2.50
Cake	£1.25
Crisps	65p
Drink	80p

....

b Chris buys a packet of crisps and a drink. Write two ways that she could pay for this with the **exact** money.

....

c Alan wants to buy one of each item. He has £5.
Does he have enough money?
Write your calculations.

☐ Yes   ☐ No

Guided

5 Work out the cost of each bill. Record your calculation.

a 250 minutes on a phone at 11 pence per minute 250 × 0.11 = £ ....

b 2745 units of electricity at 15p per unit 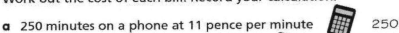 2745 × .... = £ ....

c Wages at £8 an hour for 22 hours .... × .... = £ ....

d Five friends pay £9 for a pizza. They share the cost equally. How much does each person pay?

£9 ÷ .... = 1.8 = £1. ....

Practice

6 Work out the total amounts. Record your calculation.

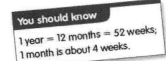
You should know
1 year = 12 months = 52 weeks;
1 month is about 4 weeks.

a Rent at £750 per month for a year ....

b Saving £15 per week for a year ....

c A newspaper costs 60p on weekdays, £1 on Saturdays and £1.20 on Sundays.
Work out the cost of having a newspaper every day for 2 weeks.

£ ....

d Lois buys 5 magazines @ £3.75 each.
How much change does she get from £20?

£ ....

e Nick bought four large cakes. He paid £10.
How much was each cake?

£ ....

7 Molly earns £700 a month. She saves 20%.
How much does she spend?

....

Simple interest

Guided

8 How much interest will these savers have at the end of the year?

a Mari: £400 at 5% $400 \times 5 \div 100 = £$ ....

b Tomas: £450 at 4% $450 \times$ .... $\div$ .... $= £$ ....

c Zoe: £360 at 7%   .... $\times$ .... $\div$ .... $= £$ ....

d Andi: £320 at 8%   .... $= £$ ....

Practice

9 How much extra per year will these borrowers have to pay on their loan?

a Lisa: £8000 car, paying interest at 12%   ....

b Sol: £450 computer, paying interest at 11%   ....

c Liz: £180 000 house, paying interest at 6%   ....

d Tony: £1500 holiday, paying interest at 14%   ....

Repayments (interest-free loans)

Guided

10 Work out how much needs to be paid each month, after the deposit is paid.

a £400 over 6 months, £40 deposit

£400 − £40 = £360   £360 ÷ 6 = £ .... per month

b £1500 over 1 year, deposit of 20%

20% of £1500 = £ ....   £1500 − £ .... = £ ....   £ .... ÷ 12 = £ .... per month

c £2500 over 8 months, £500 deposit

.... − .... = £ .... ÷ .... = £ .... per month

Practice

11 Work out how much must be paid each month, after the deposit is paid.
Show your calculations.

a £750 over 10 months, £50 deposit

....

b £3600 over a year, 5% deposit

....

Step into GCSE

12 A car costs £5000. Ian pays a deposit of £500. He will pay the rest monthly over a year.
How much will he pay each month?

£ ....

Rounding money

Remember this
50p–99p rounds up; 49p
or less rounds down.

Guided

13 Write all the numbers on the calculator display, then round to the nearest penny.

a £240 ÷ 7 = 34.28571429 = £34.29

You should know
How to round decimals to the nearest
whole one and to one decimal place.

b £550 ÷ 9 = 61.11111111 = £ ....

c £125 ÷ 13 = ... = £ .... **d** £1100 ÷ 15 = ... = £ ....

e £12 ÷ 7 = ... = £ .... **f** £47 ÷ 8 = ... = £ ....

Practice

14 Round each amount to the nearest pound.

a £34.75 £ ....

b £54.19 £ ....

c £76.81 £ ....

d £83.45 £ ....

e £184.56 £ ....

f £365.99 £ ....

Practice

15 Round each amount to the nearest 10 pence.

a £27.34 £ ....

b £12.78 £ ....

c £72.52 £ ....

d £835.48 £ ....

e £354.09 £ ....

f £65.99 £ ....

Earning money and budgeting

Guided

16 How much does each person earn?

   a Heather works for 16 hours at £8.25 an hour.   16 × £8.25 = £..........

   b Peter works for 33 hours at £12.75 an hour.   .... × £.......... = £..........

   c Sunil earns £720 for 80 hours' work. How much per hour? £.......... ÷ .... = £.......... per hour

   d Kris earns £320 for 14 hours' work. How much per hour (round to nearest penny)?

      £.......... ÷ .... = £.......... . 85714286 = £.......... . ... per hour

Practice

17 Work out the amounts earned.

   a 32 hours at £14 per hour   **b** £2100 for 4 weeks

                     £..........   £.......... per week

   c £22 260 per year   **d** 56 hours at £19.25 per hour

               £.......... per month   £..........

   e £560 for 25 hours' work   **f** £125 for 11 hours

            £.......... per hour   £.......... per hour
                                            (to nearest 1p)

Step into GCSE

18 a Dave works 8 hours per day, 5 days per week at an hourly rate of £15. How much does he earn in a week?

                                    £...........................

   b Sarah works 6 hours a day, 6 days a week. She earns £441 in a week. What is her hourly rate?

                                    £...........................

   c Lily is 16 years old. She works on weekends and earns £80 a month. Suggest a monthly budget for Lily.

     Clothes £..........   Phone £..........   Entertainment £..........   Savings £..........

Calculating bills

19 a Here is part of Richard's electricity bill. Work out the total cost of the units used.

Electricity Bill December 2012

R Johns
2 Woodlands Drive
Cheltenham

Reading 1st December   3129 units
Reading 1st September   2572 units

Number of units used .... units   3129 – 2572 = ... units

Cost: £0.18 per unit   18 × .... = ... pence = £............ . ...

---

b Jimmy has a mobile phone.

He has to pay 11p for every minute of calls and pay 8p for every text he sends.
Last month Jimmy:
* made a total of 180 minutes of calls
* sent 250 texts.
Work out how much Jimmy had to pay last month.

Calls = £0.11 × ....   Texts = £ ....

Total = £ ....

20 Work out the total cost of a trip to the cinema.

```
3 adult cinema tickets at £8.25    = ............
2 children's tickets at £4.75      = ............
1 large popcorn at £4.99           = ............

Total                              = ............
```

£ ....

21 This is Renée's phone bill. Work out the total cost for November.

Phone Bill November 2012

R Holland
22 Regent Ave
Liverpool

Rental for November   £14.25
Minutes used in November   320
Cost: £0.12 per minute

£ ....

Don't forget!

✳ Circle the amounts of money that are correctly recorded.

£3.40p   £3.04   £5.4   £0.99p   £0.99

✳ Match the calculations to the questions.

5 rolls of wrapping paper at £2.50 each

Sally receives £32.50 for 5 hours' work. What is her hourly rate?

What is the cost of 250 minutes on a phone at 15p per minute?

20% VAT on TV costing £250

32.50 ÷ 5

250 × 0.15

5 × 2.50

250 ÷ 20

5 ÷ 32.50

250 ÷ 10 × 2

Exam-style questions

1 Tahreem buys 4 books at £4.50 each. She pays with a £20 note.
   How much change does she get?

   £ ....

2 One pencil costs £0.55. Ollie buys 10 of these pencils.
   Work out the total cost.

   £ ....

3 Work out   £10 – £4.15

   £ ....

4 Elli spent £2.95. She paid with a £10 note. How much change did she get?

   £ ....

5 Here is a table that can be used to find
   the cost of rolls of sticky tape.

   a Work out the cost of 16 rolls.

      £ ....

   b Work out the cost of 24 rolls.

      £ ....

Number of rolls	Cost
1	45p
2	90p
3	£1.35
4	£1.80
5	£2.25
6	£2.70
7	£3.15
8	£3.60
9	£4.05
10	£4.50

6 Ewan bought a car for £4000. He paid a deposit of 20%.
How much deposit did he pay?

£ ....

7 Ceris bought some items from a shop. She bought:

2 notebooks at	£3.25 each
5 pencils at	35p each
1 sharpener at	£1.05 each

How much did Ceris spend?

£ ....

8 Here is Stuart's phone bill.

Phone Bill	January 2012
S Bradley	
2 King's Meadow	
Bristol	
Rental for January	£14.75
Minutes used in January	280
Cost:	£0.15 per minute

Work out the total cost of the units used.

Work out the total cost of Stuart's phone bill for January.

£ ....

9 Work out the cost of 12 packs of biscuits at 85 pence each.

£ ....

7.1

Read, record and measure time

By the end of this section you will know how to:

* Read time on analogue and digital clocks
* Convert between 12-hour time and 24-hour time
* Use the correct notation for 24-hour times

Key points

* Before 12 o'clock midday is shown as **am**.

* After midday until midnight is shown as **pm**.

* Digital time is recorded using four digits such as 01:45 and 23 54.

* There are 24 hours in a whole day, made up of two sets of 12 hours.

Guided

1 Write these times in words, 12-hour time and 24-hour time.

a 7.30 am

half past .... / 7.30 ...... / 07: ......

b 6.15 pm

.... past .... / 6. ...... pm / 18: ......

Hint
Add 12 to get the 24-hour time.

c 3.45 am

quarter .... / .... / ....

d 8.50 pm

ten to .... / .... / 20: ......

Hint
Add 12 to get the 24-hour time.

Practice

2 Show these times on the analogue clocks. Then write the 24-hour time in the space below.

a twenty past eight in the morning

b 8.45 pm

c 2.55 am

d twenty to ten at night

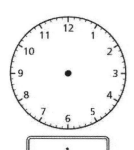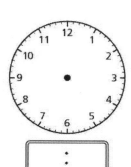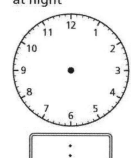

Step into GCSE

3 **a** Change these times to 24-hour times.

4.30 pm ......:......   5.20 am ......:......   11.35 pm ......:......   9.50 am ......:......

b Change these 24-hour times into 12-hour times using am or pm.

09:30 ....   22:25 ....   03:05 ....   16:44 ....

c Write these times in 12-hour am/pm and in 24-hour time.

twenty-five past eleven in the morning   five to six in the evening

....

Needs more practice ☐	Almost there ☐	I'm proficient! ☐

7.2 Use units of time

By the end of this section you will know how to:
* Read and interpret timetables
* Work out durations of time

GCSE LINKS
AF: 11.2 Time;
BF: Unit 2 17.2 Time

Key points

You should know
60 seconds = 1 minute;
60 minutes = 1 hour;
24 hours = 1 day.

* Most timetables use 24-hour digital times, so use 16:30 to show 4.30 pm.

Guided

1 Find the difference between the times shown on the two clocks.

a 7.15 + 2 hours = 9.15
9.15 + 20 min = 9.35

Time difference = ... hours ...... minutes

b 07:50 + 10 min = 08:00
08:00 + 20 min = 08:20

Time difference = ... minutes

c 4.35 + ... min = 5.00
5.00 + 1 ...... = 6.00
6.00 + ... = 6.05

Time difference = ... hour ...... minutes

d 19:25 + ... hours = 23:25
23:25 − ...... min = 23:20

Time difference = ... hours ...... minutes

Hint
When the numbers of minutes are close, sometimes it is more efficient to add on whole hours then count back.

Practice

2 Find the differences between these times.

a 3.15 am and 5.20 am   **b** 07:50 and 09:25   **c** 18:55 and 20:40

....

d 14.45 pm and 17.35 pm   **e** 07:05 and 12:55   **f** 22.30 pm and 1.15 am

....

Practice

3 Here is part of the train timetable from Eastam to Southwood.

Eastam to Southwood							
Eastam	06:11	07:05	08:22	09:25	10:09	10:56	11:43
Northlee	06:26	07:19	08:36	09:42	10:33	11:10	11:58
Westfield	06:54	07:51	09:03	10:17	11:01	11:39	12:27
Southwood	07:09	08:02	09:19	10:24	11:18	11:55	12:41

a Which train should you catch from Eastam to arrive in Southwood for 10.30 am? ....

b How long does the 08:22 train take to get from Eastam to Southwood? .... minutes

c Which train should you catch from Eastam to arrive in Westfield by 8 am? ....

d How long does the 10:09 train take to get from Northlee to Westfield? .... minutes

e Which train journey from Eastam to Southwood is faster – the 06:11 or the 10:56?
   Show your working.

   06:11 .... minutes   10:56 .... minutes   Faster ....

f Ellen arrives at Westfield station at twenty-five past eight in the morning.

   How long will she have to wait for the next train to Southwood? .... minutes

Step into GCSE

4 Here is a gym timetable.

a Find out how long each class lasts. The next class starts as the previous one finishes.

Class	Start time
Step	09:00
Circuits	10:10
Zumba	10:55
Kettle Bells	12:10
Pilates	12:50

Length of class: ....
Length of class: ....
Length of class: ....
Length of class: ....

b Lynsey wants to go to the Step and Zumba classes.
   How long will she exercise in total? .... minutes

c It takes Mike 25 minutes to get to the gym and be ready to start. What is the latest time he
   can set off to be in time for Kettle Bells?

   .... : ....

d Paulo sets off from home at 09:35 to attend the Circuits class. He spends 10 minutes in the
   changing room before the class. How long is his journey to the gym?

   .... minutes

5 These are the times in hours, minutes and seconds for three marathon runners. Who won?

Jack   Ben   Jason

02:46:17   02:45:59   02:46:09

....

7.3 Convert between units of time

By the end of this section you will know how to:
* convert between different units of time

GCSE LINKS
AF: 11.2 Time; BF: Unit 2
17.2 Time; 16+: 12.2 Speed,
distance, time

Key points

* 1 day is 24 hours; 1 week is 7 days; 1 year is 12 months.
* 1 hour is 60 minutes; 1 minute is 60 seconds.
* 1 year is 365 days, 52 weeks or 12 months.

Remember this
A leap year has an extra day —
29 February.

Practice

1 Use the numbers in the box to complete the statements about time.

| 1 | 2 | 12 | 30 | 52 | 60 | 240 | 366 |

a ...... months = 1 year   b ...... hour = ... minutes   c ...... seconds = 4 minutes

d ...... minutes = half an hour   e ...... weeks = 1 year   f ...... days in a leap year

Guided

2 Convert these units of time.

a 5 hours into minutes $5 \times 60 = 300$ minutes

b 36 months into years $36 \div 12 = 3$ years

c 60 minutes into seconds $60 \times ...... = ...$ seconds

d 416 weeks into years    ...... $\div$ ...... $=$ ...... years

e 315 days into weeks   ...... $\div$ ...... $=$ ...... weeks

f 72 hours into days 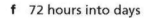   ...... $\div$ ...... $=$ ...... days

g 24 hours into **seconds** $24 \times ...... \times ...... = ...$ seconds

Practice

3 Use multiplication and division to convert these times.

a 4 days = ... hours   b 56 days = ... weeks   c 10 minutes = ... seconds

d ...... months = 6 years   e 420 minutes = ... hours   f ...... years = 48 months

Step into GCSE

4 Work out the answers.

a Eryk is at college 5 days a week for 32 weeks. How many days is that?

.... days

b The TV programme lasts $2\frac{1}{4}$ hours.
How many minutes are there in $2\frac{1}{4}$ hours?   .... minutes

c Susie cycles at a speed of 12 miles per hour. She cycles for 3 hours.
How many miles does she cycle?   .... miles

d Joe travelled 100 miles in 2 hours. How many miles per hour is that? .... miles per hour

Use calendars

7.4

By the end of this section you will know how to:

* Read, use and complete calendars
* Work out dates that are not shown

GCSE LINKS
AF: 11.2 Time;
BF: Unit 2 17.2 Time

Key points

* A calendar usually covers a whole year and each month is shown separately.
* There are 30 days in April, June, September and November.
* There are 28 days in February, except in a leap year, when there are 29.
* A **leap year** happens every four years when the year is a multiple of 4.

> **Remember this**
> A year that is a multiple of 100 is **not** a leap year unless it is a multiple of 1000.

Practice

1 Use the rhyme to fill in the number of days for each month.

January	February	March	April ....
May	June	July	August ....
September	October	November	December ....

> **Remember this**
> 30 days has September, April, June and November, all the rest have 31, except February, which has 28 days clear and 29 each leap year.

Guided

2 a Here is part of a calendar. Fill in the missing calendar dates.

June 2013						
Sun	**Mon**	**Tues**	**Wed**	**Thurs**	**Fri**	**Sat**
		4	5			8
	10	11			14	15
16	17		19			
		25		27		

> **Remember this**
> The shaded dates show the last few days of the month before and the next few days after the month displayed.

b What day of the week is 20 June 2013? ....

c What is the date of the next Tuesday after 15 June 2013? ....

d Juliana wants to have her birthday party on the Friday nearest to her birthday. Her birthday is on 12 June 2013. On which date should she have her party? ....

e What date is 2 weeks before 8 June 2013?

I week before is .... June, so 2 weeks before is .... May

f What date is 4 weeks after 25 June 2013? $25 - 2 =$ ...., so ....

g What day of the week is 27 May 2013?   27 May is ....

> **Hint**
> Use 4 weeks = 28 days.
> Example: To work out 4 weeks after 21 January: January has 31 (or 28 + 3) days:
> 21 − 3 = 18. So 4 weeks after 21 January is 18 February

Don't forget!

✳ Match the 12-hour times to the 24-hour times.

ten past ten
in the
evening

ten to nine
in the
morning

✳ Complete the time conversi\ons.

4 hours = ... minutes   36 months = ... years   .... weeks = 49 days

.... minutes = 300 seconds   .... hours = 2 days   3 hours = ... seconds

✳ When 31 March is on a Tuesday, 3 April will be on a ....

When 1 May is a Wednesday, 29 April is on a ....

Exam-style questions

1   Here is a TV timetable.

Programme	Start time
News	18:15
Sport	18:50
Cartoon	20:25
Film	21:10
Late news	23:55

a   How long is the film?   .... hours .... minutes

b   How long is the cartoon?   .... minutes

c   Jamie watches the film and the cartoon.
    What is his total viewing time?

   .... hours .... minutes

2   Here is a clock face and a digital display.
    Draw hands on the clock to show a time of
    twenty-five to eight in the evening.
    Write the numbers on the digital display to
    show the same time.

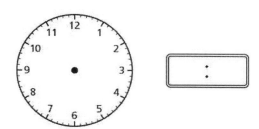

3 Write down in words the time shown on the clocks.

a

b

c

....

4 Here is part of the bus timetable from Warden Hill to Bishop's Cleeve.

Warden Hill to Bishop's Cleeve							
Warden Hill	07:15	07:55	08:35	07:15	09:55	10:35	11:15
Cheltenham	07:42	08:22	09:02	09:42	10:22	11:02	11:42
Bishop's Cleeve	08:01	08:41	09:21	10:01	10:41	11:21	12:01

a Which bus should you catch from Warden Hill to arrive in Cheltenham for 10.30 am?

....

b How long does the 07:55 bus take to get from Warden Hill to Bishop's Cleeve? .... minutes

c Which part of the journey is quicker: Warden Hill to Cheltenham or Cheltenham to Bishop's Cleeve? Show your working.

....

5 Here is part of a calendar for October 2012.

October 2012						
Sun	Mon	Tues	Wed	Thurs	Fri	Sat
	1	2	3	4	5	6
7	8	9	10	11	12	13
14	15	16	17	18	19	20

a What day of the week is 17 October? ....

b What day of the week is 21 October? ....

c What is the date two weeks after 15 October? ....

d What is the date two weeks before 9 October? ....

e What is the date four weeks after 20 October? ....

8.1 Metric and imperial measures

By the end of this section you will know how to:

* Use metric and imperial measures correctly
* Decide which metric unit of measure to use
* Decide which imperial unit of measure to use

GCSE LINKS

AF: 11.3 Metric units, 11.4 Imperial units, 2.1 Fractions of a turn, 2.2 Angles **BF:** Unit 2 17.3 Metric units, 17.4 Imperial units, 14.1 Fractions of a turn, 14.2 Angles; **16+:** 11.1 Angle facts

Key points

* Metric units are used in many countries to measure length, weight and capacity.
* Imperial measures were used in the UK until the metric system was introduced in 1963.
* The UK still uses miles instead of kilometres to measure distances.

> **You should know**
>
> Metric units
> **length / distance:** mm = millimetre; cm = centimetre; m = metre; km = kilometre;
> **capacity:** ml = millilitre; l = litre;
> **weight:** g = gram; kg = kilogram

Metric units of length, weight and capacity

Guided

1 Connect these items to the property being measured.

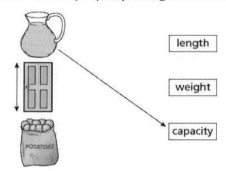

length

weight

capacity

Practice

2 Write down a suitable metric unit of measure for:

a

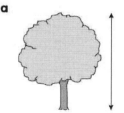

b

c

> **Hint**
> There may be more than one suitable unit in some cases.

....

....

....

d

Paris   152

e

f

....

....

....

3 Choose a suitable estimate. Draw a ring around your choice.

a The capacity of a coffee mug.	25 ml	250 ml	2.5 litres
b The weight of an apple.	18 g	180 g	1.8 kg
c The length of a classroom.	16 mm	16 cm	16 m

Imperial measures

4 Use the picture clues to work out the names of some imperial measures. Write the words in the correct column.

a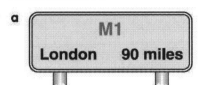

b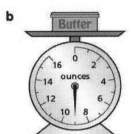

c

d

e

f

Length/distance/height	Weight	Capacity
miles	pounds	

5 Choose the correct word from the box to match each unit with its nearest metric or imperial equivalent.

metre   kilogram   pint   kilometre   gram   inch

a mile ....

b .... centimetre

c pound ....

d .... litre

e yard ....

f ounce ....

Temperature

6 The table shows the temperatures in some cities one night last December.

City	Moscow	Cape Town	London	Sydney	Vancouver
Temperature	−8°C	12°C	0°C	19°C	−3°C

a Write down the name of the city with the highest temperature. ....

b Write down the name of the city with the lowest temperature. ....

7 Use the table in question 6.

a What is the difference in temperature between London and Cape Town? .... °C

b What is the difference in temperature between Vancouver and Sydney? .... °C

Needs more practice ☐	Almost there ☐	I'm proficient! ☐

8.2 Convert between metric units

By the end of this section you will know how to:

✶ Convert between mm and cm, cm and metres, metres and km

✶ Convert between millilitres and litres, grams and kilograms

Key points

✶ Converting between metric units involves multiplying and dividing by 10, 100 or 1000.

Remember this

10 mm = 1 cm   100 cm = 1 metre   1000 m = 1 km
1000 g = 1 kg   1000 ml = 1 litre

You should know

✶ All the metric unit conversions.
✶ How to multiply and divide all numbers by 10, 100 and 1000.

Metres, centimetres and millimetres

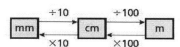

1 Convert these measurements by multiplying or dividing by 10 or 100.

Remember this

Centimetres are longer than millimetres, so there will be fewer of them – so divide.

    ÷ 10
a 30 mm = ... cm

    ÷ 10
b 75 mm = ... cm

    × 10
c 6 cm = ... mm

    × 10
d 2.5 cm = ... mm

    ÷ 10
e 124 mm = ... cm

    × 10
f 25.7 cm = ... mm

    ÷ 100
g 300 cm = ... m

    ÷ 100
h 350 cm = ... m

    ÷ 100
i 354 cm = ... m

    × 100
j 4 m = ... cm

    × 100
k 4.5 m = ... cm

    × 100
l 4.58 m = ... cm

Kilograms, kilometres and litres

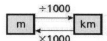

2 Multiply and divide by 1000 to convert between these units.

a 4000 m = ... km   **b** 4500 g = ... kg   **c** 4567 ml = ... litres

d 3 km = ... m   **e** 5.6 kg = ... g   **f** 2.345 litres = ... ml

g 7.2 km = ... m   **h** 6000 g = ... kg   **i** 7200 ml = ... litres

3 a Put these capacities in order. Start with the smallest amount.

   250 ml   2.5 litres   0.4 litres   1800 ml   ....

b Match the equivalent lengths.

   250 cm   25 cm   0.25 km   1250 m

   1.25 km   2.5 m   250 mm   250 m

Needs more practice [ ]   Almost there [ ]   I'm proficient! [ ]

Add and subtract units of measure

8.3

By the end of this section you will know how to:

* Add and subtract units of metric measure

> **You should know**
> How to convert between metric units.

Key points

* When adding or subtracting different units, convert one to match the other.
* The usual methods of addition and subtraction can be used.

1 Add or subtract these measurements.

a 45 mm + 24 mm

= .... mm

b 28 mm + 4.9 cm

= 28 mm + 49 mm

= .... mm

c 3 m 20 cm + 4 m 45 cm

= (3 + 4) m + (20 + 45) cm

= .... m .... cm

d 5 m 75 cm + 2 m 35 cm

= (.......... + ...) m + (.......... + ...) cm

= .... m 110 cm = ... m + 1 m 10 cm

= .... m .... cm

e 456 cm − 213 cm

= .... cm

f 6.75 m − 123 cm

= .... cm − 123 cm

= ....

Practice

2 Add and subtract these measurements, converting where you need to.

a 542 cm + 312 cm

..........cm

b 3000 g − 2745 g

..........g

c 32 mm + 12 mm + 56 mm

..........mm

d 4.5 km − 3.2 km

..........km

e 3.5 cm + 25 mm

..........mm

f 2 litres 500 ml + 300 ml

..........litres ....ml

g 2 m 45 cm − 75 cm

..........m ....cm

h 4 m 20 cm − 80 cm

..........m ....cm

Step into GCSE

3 a What is the total length of these two pieces of rope?

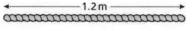

....

b What is the total distance between the library and the church?

Library ——750m—→ College ——1.4km—→ Church

....

c How much more is in the larger container?

2.6 litres

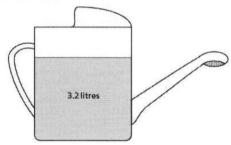
3.2 litres

....

d Add together 60 cm, 25 cm, 2 m 45 cm and 1.4 m.

....

| Needs more practice | ☐ | Almost there | ☐ | I'm proficient! | ☐ |

Read scales

8.4

By the end of this section you will know how to:

∗ Read a variety of metric scales

GCSE LINKS
AF: 11.1 Reading scales;
BF: Unit 2 17.1 Reading scales

Key points

∗ When reading scales it is important to work out how much each interval marker represents.

Guided

1 How much is each interval marker worth?
Fill in the missing numbers to complete the scales.

a 0 2 4 6 8 10   20

Each interval is worth ....

b 0   10   20   45

Each interval is worth ....

c 0   100   200   300   400

Each interval is worth ....

d

Each interval is worth .... ml

e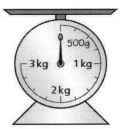

Each interval is worth .... grams

Practice

2 What measurement does each scale show?

a

.... litre .... ml

b

.... g

c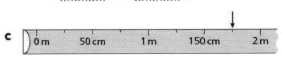

.... m .... cm

d

.... cm = ... mm

3 Draw an arrow to show the reading on each scale.

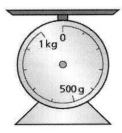

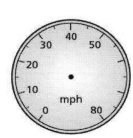

a 400 g

b 1 litre 800 ml

c 65 miles per hour

d 1 m 35 cm

e −4 °C

4 a What readings are shown? Remember to show the unit of measure.

....

b Mark each measurement with an arrow.

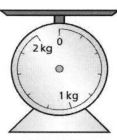

1 kg 800g   850 ml

c Estimate the reading shown on the scale.

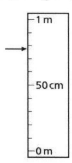

....

8.5 Draw and measure lines and angles

GCSE LINKS
AF: 2.4–2.6 Estimating, measuring and drawing angles, 11.1 Reading scales, 11.6 Accuracy of measurements; BF: Unit 2 14.4–14.6 Estimating, measuring and drawing angles, 17.1 Reading scales, 17.6 Accuracy of measurements

By the end of this section you will know how to:

* ✳ Draw and measure lines accurate to the nearest centimetre
* ✳ Draw and measure angles accurate to the nearest degree

You should know

How to round decimals to the nearest whole number.

Key points

* ✳ An angle is a measure of turn and is shown in degrees.
* ✳ A protractor is used to measure and to draw angles.
* ✳ A metric ruler shows centimetres and millimetres.
* ✳ Rulers are usually 15 cm or 30 cm long.

Measuring and drawing lines

Guided

1 Measure these lines accurate to the nearest cm.

Hint

Make sure the start of the line is at the zero marker on the ruler.

a  .... cm

b _____   .... cm

c _____   .... cm

Practice

2 Mark on each line the measurement shown.

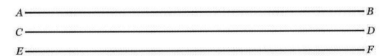

a 5 cm from A b 9 cm from C c 6 cm from F

3 a Measure the lines AB, BC and AC. Which is the longest line?

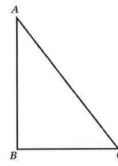

$AB =$ .... cm

$BC =$ .... cm

$AC =$ .... cm

Longest line is ....

Step into GCSE

4 Draw a line measuring exactly 12 cm, starting at the letter L. Measure to find the mid-point and mark it with the letter M.

•
L

Measuring angles

$\frac{1}{4}$ turn = right angle

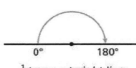

$\frac{1}{2}$ turn = straight line

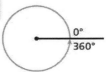

full turn

Practice

5 Write **acute** or **obtuse** under each angle.

a

....

b

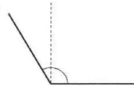

....

c

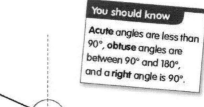

....

Guided

6 Measure each angle carefully.

a

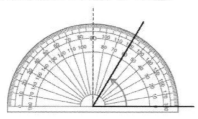

.............................°

b

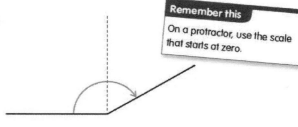

.............................°

Practice

7 Measure these angles carefully.

a

.............................°

b

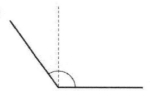

.............................°

c

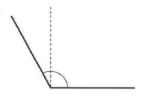

.............................°

d

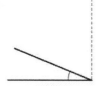

.............................°

e

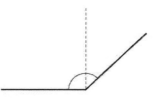

.............................°

f

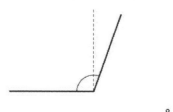

.............................°

Step into GCSE

8 Measure the angles in this triangle.

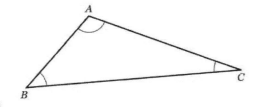

$A =$ ....° $\quad B =$ ....° $\quad C =$ ....°

Drawing angles

Guided

9 Draw and label these angles using a protractor. Start at the point shown.

a 80°

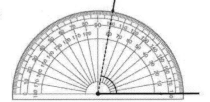

b 127°

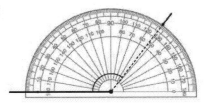

c 32°

d 127°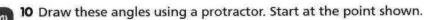

Practice

10 Draw these angles using a protractor. Start at the point shown.

a 42°

b 143°

c 162°

d 48°

11 a Measure the line *PQ* and mark the mid-point *M* on it.

P ————————————————————————————— *Q*

b At *M* draw and label an angle of 75°.

c Measure and label the other angle at *M*.

Don't forget!

✳ Join the units with what they measure.

degree gram litre mile ounce inch kilometre cm pint

capacity   angle   distance / length   temperature   weight

✳ A right angle measures .... °. An .... angle is less than 90°.

An obtuse angle is between .... ° and .... °.

✳ To convert a larger unit to a smaller unit you .... and to convert a smaller unit

to a larger unit you ....

Exam-style questions

1 Here is triangle *ABC*.

a Measure the length of the line *AB*.   .... cm

b Measure the size of angle *B*.   .... °

2 a Change 4000 millilitres into litres.   .... litres

b Change 9.5 cm into mm.   .... mm

3 Add   3 metres 45 centimetres

2 metres 50 centimetres

60 centimetres

.... metres .... cm

4 Here is line *CD*.

C ────────────────────────────── D

a Measure the length of the line *CD*.

.... cm

b At *D*, draw an angle of 52°.

5 Write down an appropriate metric unit of measure for these items.

a The length of a table.

....

b The amount of liquid in a large bucket.

....

c The weight of a small bag of peanuts.

....

6 a Write down the length shown.   **b** Write down the weight shown.

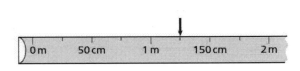

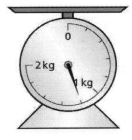

.... m .... cm

.... kg .... g

c Estimate and write down the amount shown.

.... ml

9.1 Perimeter of rectangles

By the end of this section you will know how to:

✳ Work out the perimeter of rectangles

GCSE LINKS
AF: 14.1 Perimeter
BF: Unit 1 18.1 Perimeter
16+: 13.1 Perimeter of shapes

Key points

✳ The perimeter of a shape is the distance all the way round its edge.

✳ To find the perimeter of a rectangle, add together the lengths of all the edges.

Guided

1 Write down the lengths of the sides of these rectangles. Then add them to find the perimeter.

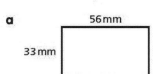

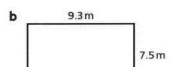

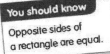

a 5 cm + 7 cm + ... cm + ... cm = ... cm

b 12 m + ... m + ... m + ... m = ... m

c .... cm + ... cm + ... cm + ... cm = ... cm

Practice

2 Work out the perimeter of these rectangles.

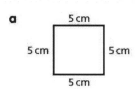

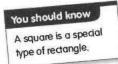

You should know
Opposite sides of a rectangle are equal.

Perimeter = ... mm   Perimeter = ... m

3 Work out the perimeter of these squares.

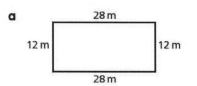

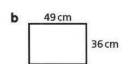

You should know
A square is a special type of rectangle.

Perimeter = ... cm   Perimeter = ... cm

4 Use the formula to find the perimeter of these shapes.

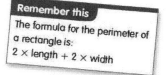

Remember this
The formula for the perimeter of a rectangle is:
2 × length + 2 × width

Perimeter = ... m   Perimeter = ... cm

Step into GCSE

5 Work out the length of the missing side.

a

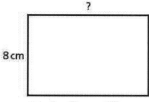

Perimeter = 40 cm

.... cm

b A square has a perimeter of 24 cm. What is the length of its sides?

.... cm

Perimeter of L shapes

Guided

6 Here is a shape made from rectangles. Work out the lengths of the missing sides.

42 + 20 = ... cm

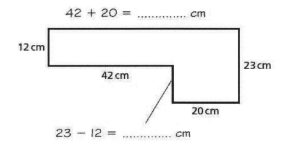

23 − 12 = ... cm

Now work out the distance all the way round the shape. This is the perimeter:

.... + ... + ... + ... + ... + ... = ... cm

Practice

7 Find the perimeter of this shape.

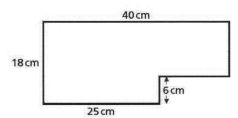

Hint

First find the length of any missing sides.

Perimeter = ... cm

Step into GCSE

8 This shape is made up of four identical squares.
Find the perimeter of the shape.

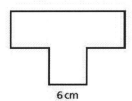

6 cm

Perimeter = ... cm

Area of rectangles

9.2

By the end of this section you will know how to:

❋ Work out the area of rectangles

GCSE LINKS
AF: 14.2 Area;
BF: Unit 1 18.2 Area;
16+: 13.2 Area of shapes

Key points

❋ The area of a shape is the amount of space inside it.

❋ To find the area of a rectangle multiply the width by the length.

❋ To find the area of a shape made from rectangles, add the areas of the individual rectangles.

Guided

1 Find the area of these rectangles by counting the squares.
Multiply the two lengths together to check your answer.

Remember this

Area is recorded in square units, e.g. mm², cm², m².

a
3 cm
2 cm

b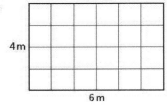
4 m
6 m

c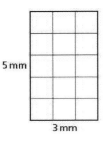
5 mm
3 mm

area = ... cm²

3 × 2 = ... cm²

area = ... m²

.... × .... = ... m²

area = ... mm²

.... × .... = ... mm²

Practice

2 Find the area of these rectangles using the formula.

a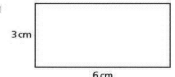
3 cm
6 cm

b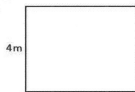
4 m
5 m

c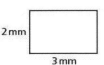
2 mm
3 mm

Remember this

Area of rectangle = width × length.

Area = ... cm²

Area = ... m²

Area = ... mm²

Step into GCSE

3 a Work out the total area of this shape.

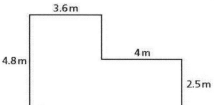
3.6 m
4.8 m
4 m
2.5 m

Area = ... m²

b Work out the shaded area of this shape.

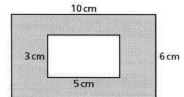
10 cm
3 cm
5 cm
6 cm

Hint

Find the difference between the areas of the larger and the smaller rectangles.

Area = ... cm²

Don't forget!

* To find the perimeter of a rectangle ....

* To find the area of a rectangle ....

Exam-style questions

1 Here is a shaded rectangle drawn on a grid of centimetre squares.

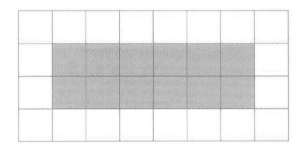

a Find the perimeter of the rectangle.

.... cm

b Find the area of the rectangle.

.... cm²

2 Here is a shaded shape drawn on a grid of centimetre squares.

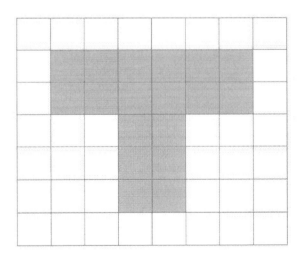

a Find the perimeter of the shape.

.... cm

b Find the area of the shape.

.... cm²

3 Here is a shape made from rectangles.

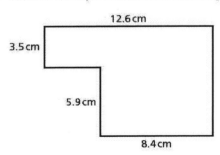

Work out the perimeter of the shape.

.... cm

71

10.1 Volume of cuboids

GCSE LINKS
AF: 20.4 Volumes; BF: Unit 2
19.3 Volume of prisms; Unit 3
9.3 Volume; 16+: 16.2 Volume
of cuboids and prisms

By the end of this section you will know how to:

﹡ Find the volume of a cuboid using the formula:
   volume = length × width × height

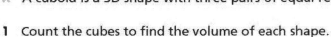

3 dimensions

You should know
How to find the area of a rectangle.

Key points

﹡ **Volume** is the space a 3D shape takes up.

﹡ **3D** means 3 dimensions: length (*l*), width (*w*), height (*h*).

﹡ A cuboid is a 3D shape with three pairs of equal rectangular faces.

Guided

1 Count the cubes to find the volume of each shape.

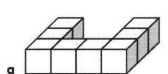

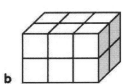

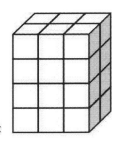

Remember this
Volume is recorded in cubic units, e.g. mm³, cm³, m³.

a

b   3 × 2 × 2 = ...

c   ...... × ...... × ...... = ...

volume = ... cm³   volume = ... cm³   volume = ... cm³

Practice

2 Find the volume of each cuboid by using the formula.

Remember this
Volume of cuboid = length × width × height.

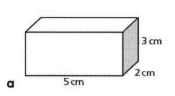

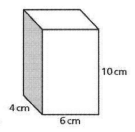

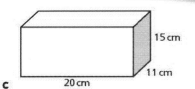

a   5 cm, 3 cm, 2 cm

b   6 cm, 4 cm, 10 cm

c   20 cm, 15 cm, 11 cm

Volume = ...   Volume = ...   Volume = ...

= .... cm³   = ... cm³   = ... cm³

3 Find the volume of each cuboid by using the formula.

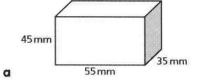

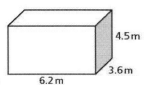

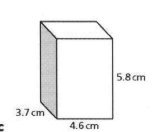

a   45 mm, 55 mm, 35 mm

b   6.2 m, 4.5 m, 3.6 m

c   3.7 cm, 4.6 cm, 5.8 cm

Volume = ...   Volume = ...   Volume = ...

= .... mm³   = ... m³   = ... cm³

Cubes

4 a Find the volume of each cube. Record your answers in the table.

Length of edges	*l*	*w*	*h*	Volume
1 cm	1	1	1	1 cm³
2 cm	2	2	2	
3 cm	3			
4 cm	4			
5 cm	5			
6 cm	6			
7 cm	7			
8 cm	8			
9 cm	9			
10 cm	10			

b A cube has a volume of 125 cm³.
What is the length of each edge? .... cm

c A cube has a volume of 1000 m³.
What is the length of each edge? .... m

Don't forget!

✳ To find the volume of a cuboid ....

✳ A cube is a special type of cuboid because ....

Exam-style questions

1 Work out the volume of this cuboid.

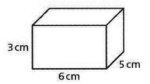

.... cm³

2 Work out the volume of this cube.

.... m³

3 Work out the volume of this cuboid.

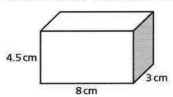

.... cm³

11.1 Read and interpret real-life charts

GCSE LINKS
AF: 3.5 Two-way tables, 12.5 Line graphs, 22.2 Conversion graphs; BF: Unit 1 1.5 Two-way tables, 2.5 Line graphs; Unit 2 12.2 Conversion graphs; 16+: 8.4 Everyday graphs, 19.3 Two-way tables

By the end of this section you will know how to:

* Read and interpret conversion charts, mileage charts, line graphs and everyday tables

Key points

* Scale is important in every graph and chart.
* Charts and graphs are often used in real-life to display information clearly.
* It is important to be able to read and understand a variety of charts and graphs.

Practice

1 The table shows the languages some students are learning.

	French	Spanish	German	Russian
Ali	✓			
Mori		✓	✓	✓
Boris	✓			✓
Juli	✓		✓	

a Which students are learning exactly two languages? ....

b Who is learning the most languages? ....

c Who is learning German but not Spanish? ....

d Who is learning the fewest languages? ....

e Which students are learning French but not German? ....

Step into GCSE

2 The table shows the numbers of boys and girls in Year 10 and Year 11.

	Boys	Girls	Total
Y10	64		120
Y11	65	72	
Total			

> **You should know**
> How to add and subtract whole numbers.

a Complete the table.

b How many more pupils are in Year 11 than Year 10? ....

c How many more boys than girls are there in total? ....

d How can you check that your overall total is correct?

....

e Check your final total is correct.

Guided

3 Here is a diagram showing the distances, in miles, between some places. Complete the mileage chart for this information.

Gloucester   Birmingham   Liverpool   Carlisle

         86   98   118

Gloucester			
86	Birmingham		
		Liverpool	
			Carlisle

Gloucester to Liverpool = 86 + 98 = ... miles

Birmingham to Carlisle = 98 + ... = ... miles

Gloucester to Carlisle = ... + ... + ... = ... miles

Practice

4 This mileage chart gives the distances, in miles, between each of these places.

Newcastle			
19	Durham		
39	26	Middlesbrough	
103	90	71	Leeds

a Write down the distance between Durham and Leeds. ....

b Write down the distance between Newcastle and Middlesbrough. ....

c Which two towns are the closest to each other? .... and ....

d Mei-Ling travels from Newcastle to Middlesbrough in the morning, then continues to Leeds in the afternoon. What is the total distance she has travelled?

.... miles

5 Use the mileage chart in question 4 to answer these questions.

a How many miles further from Durham is it to Leeds than to Middlesbrough?

.... miles

b How much further is it travelling from Newcastle to Leeds, visiting Durham and Middlesbrough on the way, rather than the direct distance? Show your working out.

.... miles

Conversion charts

6 Here is a table that can be used to convert between miles and kilometres.

Guided

a Change 3 miles into kilometres. .... km

b Change 6.4 km into miles. .... miles

c Change 15 miles into km.

15 miles = 10 miles + 5 miles

= 16 km + ... km = ... km

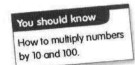
Hint
You can also use:
kilometres = 1.6 × miles.

Miles	Kilometres
1	1.6
2	3.2
3	4.8
4	6.4
5	8.0
10	16
50	80
100	160

d Change 320 km into miles.

320 km = 3.2 km × 100

= .... miles × 100 = ... miles

You should know
How to multiply numbers by 10 and 100.

e Change 64 miles into km.

64 miles = 50 miles + 10 miles + 4 miles = ... km + ... km + 6.4 km = ... km

f Change 48 km into miles.

48 = 4.8 × .... km = ... miles × .... = ... miles

7 Here is a table that can be used to change between pounds (£) and Australian dollars ($).

Practice

a Change 4 pounds (£) to Australian dollars ($).

$ ....

b Change 7.50 Australian dollars ($) to pounds (£).

£ ....

c Change 600 pounds (£) to Australian dollars ($).

$ ....

d Change 109 pounds (£) to Australian dollars ($).

$ ....

Pounds (£)	Australian dollars ($)
1	1.50
2	3.00
3	4.50
4	6.00
5	7.50
6	9.00
7	10.50
8	12.00
9	13.50
10	15.00
100	150.00

8 Here is a table that can be used to find the cost of bags of oranges.

Number of bags	Cost
1	85p
2	£1.70
3	£2.55
4	£3.40
5	£4.25
6	£5.10
7	£5.95
8	£6.80
9	£7.65
10	£8.50

a Work out the cost of 15 bags of oranges.

£ ....

b Work out the cost of 20 bags of oranges.

£ ....

c Work out the cost of 28 bags of oranges.

£ ....

Line graphs

Practice

9 This line graph shows the average daily temperature over a year.

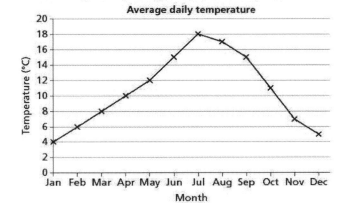

a Which month has the highest average temperature? ....

b Which month has the lowest average temperature? ....

c Which two months have the same average temperature? .... and ....

Timetables

Practice

10 Here is part of the train timetable from Honeybourne to Pittville.

Honeybourne to Pittville							
Honeybourne	11 05	11 25	12 05	12 25	13 05	13 25	14 05
Landsdown	11 28	11 48	12 28	12 48	13 28	13 48	14 28
Pittville	11 42	12 02	12 42	13 02	13 42	14 02	14 42

a Which train should you catch from Honeybourne to arrive in Pittville just after 13 00?

....

b How long does the 11 05 train take to get from Honeybourne to Pittville? ....

c How long does the 13 25 train take to get from Honeybourne to Landsdown? ....

Read bar charts and dual bar charts

11.2

GCSE LINKS
AF: 12.3 Bar charts, 12.4 Comparative bar charts; BF: Unit 1 2.3 Bar charts, 2.4 Comparative bar charts; 16+: Dual bar charts

By the end of this section you will know how to:
* Read and use bar charts and dual bar charts

Key points

* Scale is important in every graph and bar chart.
* Dual bar charts show two sets of information and are used to compare data.

1 Here is a bar chart of the number of each type of coin in a savings box.

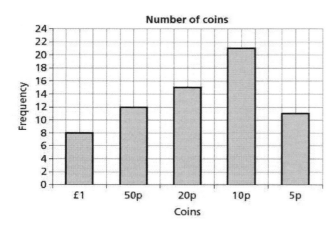

Hint
When a scale is in 2s, half a square means 1.

a How many £1 coins are in the box? ....

b How many 10p coins are in the box? ....

c How many more 20p coins than 5p coins are there? ....

d How much are the 50p coins worth? ....

e Work out the total number of coins in the box. ....

Dual bar charts

2 Mr Hall recorded the number of pupils in each year group. The dual bar chart shows this information.

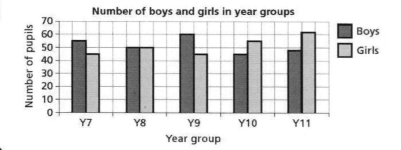

You should know
How to read and draw bar charts.

Hint
When a scale is in 10s, half a square means 5.

a How can you tell which year groups have more boys than girls?

The Boys bar is .... than the .... bar.

b Which year groups have more girls than boys? .... and ....

c Approximately how many pupils are in Year 11?

Boys: between 40 and ...., approx. ....

Girls: between .... and ......, approx. ....

Total of boys and girls: approx. .... + ... = ... pupils

d How many boys are in Year 7? ....   **e** How many girls are in Year 9? ....

3 Use the dual bar chart in question 2.

a How many pupils are in Year 7 altogether? ....

b How many pupils are in Years 7–9 in total? ....

Step into GCSE

Needs more practice ☐   Almost there ☐   I'm proficient! ☐

11.3 Draw bar charts

By the end of this section you will know how to:
* Draw and use bar charts

Key points

* Scale is important in every graph and bar chart.
* Bars should always be the same width in bar charts.

1 Draw a bar chart to show the information in this table.

Colours of cars in the car park

Guided

Colour	Frequency
red	6
blue	5
black	10
silver	8
white	3

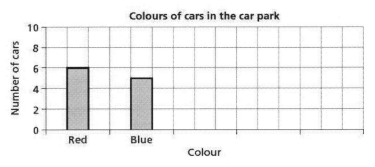

red: 6 cars → 3 squares

blue: 5 cars → $2\frac{1}{2}$ ....

black: 10 cars → .... squares

silver: 8 cars → ....

white: 3 cars → ....

Practice

2 Draw a bar chart to show the information in the table.

Favourite fruits

Fruit	Frequency
pineapple	12
melon	7
peach	9
strawberry	15
plum	4

> **Remember this**
> The bars in a bar chart must be the same width and spaced evenly.

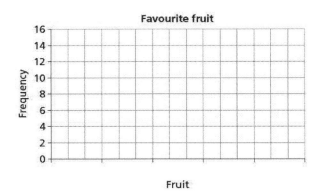

Step into GCSE

3 Use the table or the bar chart in question 2 to answer these questions.

a Which fruit was the most popular? ....

b How many people, altogether, chose pineapple or peach as their favourite? ....

c Which fruit was the least popular? ....

d How many more people liked strawberries than melons? ....

Don't forget!

✳ I need to understand charts and graphs because ....

✳ Join the type of chart to where it could be found in real life.

Bar chart   Distance chart   Conversion chart   Information table

Currency exchange   Library opening times   Results of a survey   In a road atlas

✳ The scale on a graph shows .... each square is worth. If one square means 2,

two squares mean .... and half a square means ....

Exam-style questions

1 Gary carried out a survey on where people prefer to do their shopping. Here are his results.

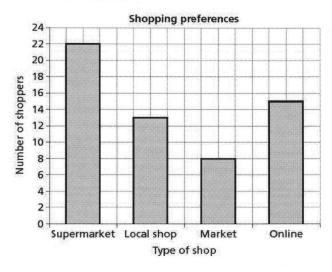

a What is the most popular type of place to shop?

....

b How many people prefer to shop online?

....

c Work out how many people were surveyed.

....

2 Amber carried out a survey of the animals people want to see at the zoo. Here are her results.

Animal	Frequency
elephant	10
lion	8
tiger	7
crocodile	5
snake	2

Draw a bar chart to display this information on the grid.

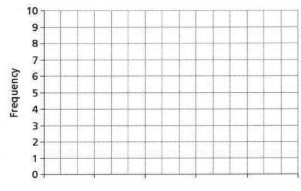

3 Jake carried out a survey to compare the rainfall in different cities.
Here are his results.

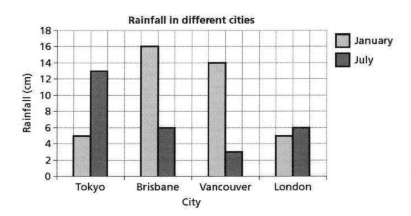

a What is the average rainfall in Brisbane in July? .... cm

b What is the average rainfall in Tokyo in January? .... cm

c Which city has a similar amount of rainfall in both January and July? ....

d Which cities have more rainfall in January than in July? .... and ....

e Which of these cities has the most rainfall in total?

....

4 This mileage chart gives the distances, in miles, between each of these cities.

Cardiff			
41	Swansea		
99	73	Aberystwyth	
177	155	82	Bangor

a Write down the distance between Aberystwyth and Bangor. .... miles

b Write down the distance between Swansea and Cardiff. .... miles

c How much further is it from Swansea to Bangor than from Cardiff to Aberystwyth?

.... miles

d Lois travelled from Cardiff to Bangor via Swansea then went to Aberystwyth.
How far did she travel in total?

.... miles

5 Here is some information about swimming pool opening times.

Day	Daytime	Evening
Sunday	10:00 – 16.30	Closed
Monday	09:00 – 13:00	17:00 – 20:00
Tues – Thurs	08:30 – 16:30	Closed
Friday	09:00 – 16:00	18:00 – 20:30
Saturday	09:30 – 18:00	

a On which day does the swimming pool open at 09:30? ....

b What are the opening times on a Wednesday? ....

c How long is the daytime opening on Monday? ....

d On which day is the pool open for the longest time? Show your working.

....

6 Here is a table that can be used to change between pounds (£) and dollars ($).

Pounds (£)	1	2	3	4	5	6	7	8	9	10	100
Dollars ($)	1.55	3.10	4.65	6.20	7.75	9.30	10.85	12.40	13.95	15.50	155

a Change 6 pounds (£) to dollars ($). $ ....

b Change 12.40 dollars ($) to pounds (£). £ ....

c Change 20 pounds (£) to dollars ($). $ ....

d Change 120 pounds (£) into dollars ($). $ ....

7 Here is a table that can be used to find the weight of one pound (£1) coins.

Number of coins	Weight in grams
1	9.5 g
2	19 g
3	28.5 g
4	38 g
5	47.5 g
6	57 g
10	95 g

a How much do five pound coins weigh? .... g

b How many pound coins weigh 57 g? ....

c How much do 100 pound coins weigh? .... g

d How many pound coins weigh 190 g? ....

Section A (Calculator)

Time: 1 hour

Edexcel publishes official Sample Assessment Material on its website. This Practice Exam Paper has been written to help you practise what you have learned and may not be representative of a real exam paper.

1 a Here is the line *PQ*.

P ———————————————————————— *Q*

Measure the length of the line *PQ*.

.... cm

(1)

b Here is the line *AB*.

A ———————————— *B*

At *A* draw an angle of 68°.

(1)

(Total for Question 1 is 2 marks)

2 Here is a number line.

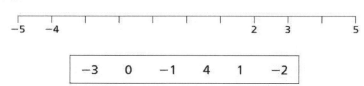

| −3 | 0 | −1 | 4 | 1 | −2 |

a Write the numbers from the box in the correct places on the number line. Some have been done for you.

(1)

Use your number line to work out

b −4 + 6 =

....

(1)

c 2 − 5 =

....

(1)

(Total for Question 2 is 3 marks)

3 Here is a cuboid.

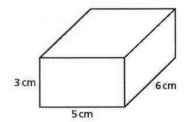

Diagram **NOT**
accurately drawn

3 cm

6 cm

5 cm

Work out the volume of this cuboid.

.... cm³

(Total for Question 3 is 2 marks)

4 Mr Cripps recorded how many students were receiving music tuition in different instruments.
The dual bar chart shows his results.

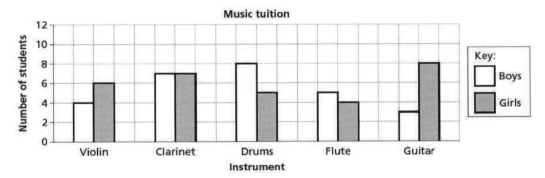

a How many boys learn the drums?

.... boys

(1)

b How many more girls than boys learn the guitar?

.... girls

(1)

c Which is the most popular instrument?

....

(2)

(Total for Question 4 is 4 marks)

5 a Change 6.7 litres into millilitres.

.... ml

(1)

b Change 506 centimetres into metres.

.... m

(1)

(Total for Question 5 is 2 marks)

6 Colin bought some items at the garden centre.

He bought   3 seed trays at   £2.49 each

4 shrubs at   £6.75 each

1 bag of potting compost at   £4.95 each

a How much did Colin spend?

£ ....
(3)

b How much change should Colin get from £50?

£ ....
(1)

(Total for Question 6 is 4 marks)

---

7 Here is a list of numbers.

6   11   15   27   30

From the list of numbers

a write down a multiple of 9

....
(1)

b write down a factor of 24

....
(1)

c write down a prime number

....
(1)

(Total for Question 7 is 3 marks)

---

8 Here is part of a calendar for April 2013.

| April 2013 | | | | | | |
Sun	Mon	Tues	Wed	Thurs	Fri	Sat
	1	2	3	4	5	6
7	8	9	10	11	12	13
14	15	16	17	18	19	20

a What day of the week is the 24th April?

....
(1)

b What is the date four weeks after the 5th April?

....
(2)

(Total for Question 8 is 3 marks)

9 a Here is a rectangle.

Diagram **NOT** accurately drawn

4.5 cm

8 cm

Work out the area of this rectangle.

.... cm²

(2)

b Here is a shape.

15 cm

Diagram **NOT** accurately drawn

10 cm

6 cm

8 cm

Work out the perimeter of this shape.

.... cm

(2)

(Total for Question 9 is 4 marks)

10 A jacket costs £90 plus VAT at 20%.
Find 20% of £90

£ ....

(Total for Question 10 is 2 marks)

11 a Use your calculator to work out $112.95 \div 15.06$

....

(1)

b Write 7.829 correct to one decimal place.

....

(1)

(Total for Question 11 is 2 marks)

12 Write down an appropriate unit of measure for these items.

a The length of a short-distance running track.

....

(1)

b The capacity of a tea cup.

....

(1)

(Total for Question 12 is 2 marks)

13 This distance chart gives the distances, in miles, between each of these cities.

Penzance				
78	Plymouth			
110	45	Exeter		
194	124	80	Bristol	
223	153	116	40	Gloucester

   a Write down the distance between Plymouth and Bristol.

.... miles

(1)

   b Write down the distance between Exeter and Penzance.

.... miles

(1)

Lucy travels from Plymouth to Gloucester, stopping at Exeter and Bristol on the way.

   c Work out the total distance Lucy has travelled.

.... miles

(2)

(Total for Question 13 is 4 marks)

14 Here is part of the bus timetable from Southampton to Winchester.

Southampton to Winchester						
Southampton	07:15	08:05	08:45	09:10	09:30	09:50
Chandler's Ford	07:47	08:38	09:18	09:38	09:58	10:18
Otterbourne	07:57	08:47	09:27	09:47	10:07	10:27
Winchester	08:30	09:15	09:50	10:10	10:30	10:50

   a Which bus should you catch from Southampton to arrive in Winchester for 10 am?

....

(1)

   b How long does the 08:05 bus take to get from Chandler's Ford to Otterbourne?

....

(1)

   c How long does the 09:50 bus take to get from Chandler's Ford to Winchester?

....

(1)

(Total for Question 14 is 3 marks)

15 Here is part of Jack's water bill.

Water Bill	September 2012
J. Ashcroft Greenfield Farm Billinge	
Reading 1st May	1234 units
Reading 1st August	2016 units
Number of units used	_____ units
Cost: £0.05 per unit	

Work out the total cost of the units used.

£ ....

(Total for Question 15 is 4 marks)

16 Here is a table that can be used to change between miles and kilometres.

Miles	Kilometres
5	8
10	16
15	24
20	32
25	40
30	48

a Change 25 miles into kilometres.

.... km

(1)

b Change 24 kilometres into miles.

.... miles

(1)

c Change 200 miles into kilometres.

.... km

(2)

(Total for Question 16 is 4 marks)

17 The table shows the temperatures in some countries in February.

Country	Temperature (°C)
UK	5°
Mexico	14°
Canada	−10°
Ukraine	−5°
Peru	23°

a Write down the country with the highest temperature.

....

(1)

b Write down the country with the lowest temperature.

....

(1)

(Total for Question 17 is 2 marks)

TOTAL FOR SECTION A IS 50 MARKS

Section B (Non-Calculator)

Time: 30 minutes

Edexcel publishes official Sample Assessment Material on its website. This Practice Exam Paper has been written to help you practise what you have learned and may not be representative of a real exam paper.

1 Max carried out a survey on people's favourite Olympic events.
Here are his results.

Favourite event	Frequency
athletics	12
swimming	10
cycling	15
sailing	7
gymnastics	9

Draw a bar chart to display this information on the grid.

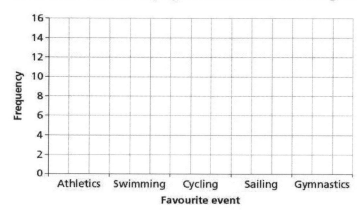

(Total for Question 1 is 3 marks)

2 a Work out 24.5 + 12.7

....

(1)

b Work out 732 − 89

....

(1)

c Work out 73 × 100

....

(1)

d Work out 72 ÷ 10

....

(1)

(Total for Question 2 is 4 marks)

3 a Write 836 in words.

....
(1)

b Write 836 to the nearest hundred.

....
(1)

(Total for Question 3 is 2 marks)

---

4 a Work out 136×4

....
(1)

b Work out $702 \div 6$

....
(1)

(Total for Question 4 is 2 marks)

---

5 a Here is a clock face.

Draw the hands on the clock face to show a time of **twenty-five past nine**.

(1)

b Here is a digital clock face.

Write the numbers on the face to show **ten to eight in the evening**.

(1)

(Total for Question 5 is 2 marks)

---

6 Alex bought 3 pizzas for £2.50 each. He paid with a £10 note.
Work out how much change he should get.

£ ....

(Total for Question 6 is 2 marks)

7 a Work out $\frac{4}{11} + \frac{3}{11}$

....
(1)

b Work out $\frac{7}{8} - \frac{3}{8}$

....
(1)

(Total for Question 7 is 2 marks)

8 a Write $\frac{1}{10}$ as a decimal.

....
(1)

b Write 0.7 as a percentage.

.... %
(1)

c Write 60% as a fraction.
Write your answer in its simplest form.

....
(2)

(Total for Question 8 is 4 marks)

9 a Work out 5% of £60

£ ....
(1)

b Work out $\frac{1}{3}$ of 30

....
(1)

(Total for Question 9 is 2 marks)

10 a Write these numbers in order of size. Start with the smallest number.

54   39   8   122   40   109

....
(1)

b Write these numbers in order of size. Start with the smallest number.

8.9   0.79   9.8   0.09   7.07   7.2

....
(1)

c Write these numbers in order of size. Start with the smallest number.

−3   7   0   −10   4   −1

....
(1)

(Total for Question 10 is 3 marks)

11 a Use rounding to the nearest 10 to find an approximate answer to this question.

49 × 21 = approximately .... × .... = ...

(1)

b Write a subtraction calculation you could use to check this addition.
24.56 + 18.05 = 42.61

....

(1)

(Total for Question 11 is 2 marks)

12 a Here are some scales.

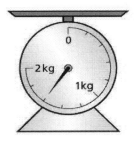

What reading do the scales show? Write the unit in your answer.

....

(1)

b Here is a measuring jug.

Draw an arrow on the jug to show a reading of 750 ml.

(1)

(Total for Question 12 is 2 marks)

TOTAL FOR SECTION B IS 30 MARKS
TOTAL FOR PAPER IS 80 MARKS

Answers

1 Integers

1.1 Read, write, order and compare positive integers

1   **a**   four hundred and fifty-six   **b**   five hundred and nine
2   **a**   two hundred and seventy-four   **b**   three hundred and fifty
   c   six hundred and five   **d**   four hundred and eighteen
   e   nine hundred and ninety-nine
3   **a**   497   **b**   319   **c**   803   **d**   930
4   **a**   300 + 80 + 6   **b**   400 + 0 + 5
   c   700 + 10 + 0   **d**   900 + 40 + 2
5   **a**   800 + 20 + 9   **b**   400 + 70 + 1
   c   600 + 20 + 0   **d**   700 + 0 + 6
6   **a**   is less than   **b**   is more than   **c**   is less than
   d   is less than   **e**   is more than   **f**   is more than
7   **a**   285, 313, 465, 639   **b**   637, 673, 736, 763
   c   415, 423, 432, 451
8   **a**   943   **b**   349   **c**   394
9   **a**   700 or seven hundred
   b   four thousand, seven hundred and eight
   c   9417

1.2 Add and subtract positive integers

1   **a**   50 + 10 = 60
   b   40 + 50 + 6 + 4 = 90 + 10 = 100
   c   20 + 40 + 30 + 5 + 5 = 2 = 90 + 12 = 102
2   **a**   7   **b**   16   **c**   20   **d**   54   **e**   14   **f**   68
3   81 + 19   31 + 69   93 + 7   79 + 21   59 + 41   9 + 91
4   **a**   716   **b**   1112   **c**   542
5   **a**   847   **b**   966   **c**   1091   **d**   933   **e**   901   **f**   823
6   **a**   444   **b**   224   **c**   253
7   **a**   288   **b**   250   **c**   626   **d**   324   **e**   244   **f**   446
8   **a**   1056   **b**   56   **c**   871

1.3 Multiply and divide by 10, 100 and 1000

1   **a**   340   **b**   1230   **c**   56 000   **d**   37 000
2   **a**   570   **b**   5830   **c**   1200   **d**   600
   e   7200   **f**   37 600   **g**   60 000   **h**   752 000
   i   360 000
3   **a**   12   **b**   265   **c**   48   **d**   7
4   **a**   5   **b**   29   **c**   500   **d**   4   **e**   60
   f   25   **g**   83   **h**   3   **i**   12
5   **a**   450   **b**   45   **c**   4500   **d**   450   **e**   45
   f   45 000   **g**   45   **h**   450
6   **a**   720 = 72 × 10 = 7200 ÷ 10 or 72 000 ÷ 100
   b   100   **c**   32 000

1.4 Multiplication and division facts up to 10 × 10

1   **a**   12, 24, 18, 30, 21, 45, 28, 25, 36, 36, 40, 81
   b   3, 4, 9, 5, 7, 9, 7, 5, 36, 36, 40, 9
2   **a**   5 × 4 = 20, 20 ÷ 4 = 5, 20 ÷ 5 = 4
   b   4 × 7 = 28, 28 ÷ 7 = 4, 28 ÷ 4 = 7
   c   15 ÷ 5 = 3, 3 × 5 = 15, 5 × 3 = 15
3   **a**   3, 24 ÷ 3 = 8, 3 × 8 = 24, 8 × 3 = 24
   b   54, 9 × 6 = 54, 54 ÷ 9 = 6, 54 ÷ 6 = 9
   c   9, 63 ÷ 9 = 7, 7 × 9 = 63, 9 × 7 = 63
4   **a**   6 × 10 = 60   **b**   4 × 3 × 10 = 12 × 10 = 120
5   **a**   240   **b**   210   **c**   450   **d**   720
6   **a**   620   **b**   5   **c**   6200

1.5 Multiply and divide by a single digit

1   **a**   120   **b**   1518   **c**   1516
2   **a**   104   **b**   144   **c**   595
   d   1090   **e**   3138   **f**   3627
3   **a**   181   **b**   135   **c**   170
4   **a**   158   **b**   147   **c**   134
   d   162   **e**   68   **f**   59
5   **a**   30   **b**   683   **c**   374

1.6 Round to the nearest 10, 100 and 1000

Town	1 Nearest 10 miles	Nearest 100 miles	2 Nearest 10 km	Nearest 100 km
Bangor	270	300	430	400
Birmingham	120	100	190	200
Bristol	120	100	190	200
Cardiff	150	200	230	200
Glasgow	410	400	650	600
Manchester	200	200	310	300

3   Lakeside 3000; Fieldcourt 7000; Castle Hill 4000; Millbrook 5000; Meadow Bank 8000; Broadoak 1000

1.7 Find multiples and factors and identify prime numbers

1

×	2	3	4	5	6	7	8	9	10
2	4	6	8	10	12	14	16	18	20
3	6	9	12	15	18	21	24	27	30
4	8	12	16	20	24	28	32	36	40
5	10	15	20	25	30	35	40	45	50
6	12	18	24	30	36	42	48	54	60
7	14	21	28	35	42	49	56	63	70
8	16	24	32	40	48	56	64	72	80
9	18	27	36	45	54	63	72	81	90
10	20	30	40	50	60	70	80	90	100

2   **a**   (5), 10, 15, 20, 25, 30, 35, 40, 45, 50
   b   (6), 12, 18, 24, 30, 36, 42, 48, 54, 60
   c   (9), 18, 27, 36, 45, 54, 63, 72, 81, 90
3   **a**   1 × 12, 2 × 6, 3 × 4   **b**   1 × 30, 2 × 15, 3 × 10, 5 × 6
   c   1 × 16, 2 × 8, 4 × 4
4   **a**   1, 2, 3, 4, 6, 12   **b**   1, 2, 3, 5, 6, 10, 15, 30   **c**   1, 2, 4, 8, 16
5   **a**   1, 2, 3, 6   **b**   1, 2   **c**   1, 2, 4
6   **a**   6   **b**   2   **c**   4
7   2, 3, 5, 7, 11, 13, 17, 19, 23, 29
8   **a**   18   **b**   4   **c**   11   **d**   10
   e   15 is a factor of 45 or 45 is a multiple of 15

1.8 Understand and use negative numbers

1   A 10°C, B 2°C, C −4°C, D −13°C
2   **a**   14°C, 6°C, 0°C, −9°C   **b**   8°C, 0°C, −6°C, −15°C
3   **a**   −4, −2, 0, 6, 9   **b**   7, 3, 0, −8, −11
4   **a**   −1   **b**   −5   **c**   0   **d**   −4   **e**   3   **f**   −4
5   **a**   −2   **b**   −3   **c**   −6   **d**   0   **e**   −10   **f**   −11

Don't forget!

* integer → whole number; negative number → number less than zero; multiple of 10 → number in the 10 times table; factor → number that divides exactly into another number; prime number → number divisible only by itself and 1
* −3 + 5 = 2; 2 − 5 = −3; −5 + 3 = −2; −1 − 4 = −5
* 54 ÷ 6 = 9; 62 × 10 = 620; 8 × 9 = 72; 6200 ÷ 100 = 62
* up; down

Exam-style questions

1   **a**   240   **b**   64   **c**   360
2   **a**   951   **e**   344
3   **a**   1024   **b**   57
4   **a**   three hundred and sixty-seven   **b**   370   **c**   400
5   **a**   258, 285, 399, 528   **b**   −11, −3, 0, 6, 8

6 a 10, 15   **b** 7, 19   **c** 6, 12   **d** 14, 16   **e** 9

7 a 12°C, −8°C

b, c

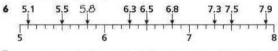

−2°C   5°C

2 Decimals

2.1 Read, write and order decimals

1 $\frac{5}{10} = 0.5$ **b** $\frac{6}{100} = 0.06$ **c** $\frac{8}{10} + \frac{3}{100} = 0.83$

2 a 7 columns (or rows)
  b 4 squares
  c 5 columns (or rows) + 5 squares
  d 6 columns (or rows) + 2 squares
  e 1 column (or row) + 9 squares
  f 9 columns (or rows) + 1 square

3 0.04, 0.19, 0.55, 0.62, 0.7, 0.91

4 a 0.5, 0.56, 0.6, 0.65, 0.7, 0.76
  b 2.19, 2.35, 2.4, 2.5, 2.53

5 a 0.7, 3.5, 3.9, 4.8
  b 3.67, 3.76, 4.28, 4.82
  c 4.89, 4.98, 6.2, 6.7
  d 18.58, 18.6, 18.7, 18.75
  e 24.57, 24.7, 24.75, 24.9

6 5.1   5.5   5.8   6.3 6.5   6.8   7.3 7.5   7.9

7 5.1 5.2 5.3 5.4 5.5 5.6 5.7 5.8 5.9
   5.15   5.25 5.33   5.45 5.55   5.68 5.75   5.85   5.99

8 a W White 15.09, R Red 15.56, B Blue 15.65, G Green 15.7
  b L Legge 16.5, B Speede 16.49, T Highe 16.07, M Springer 15.99

2.2 Add and subtract decimals

1 a 9.2   **b** 9.30   **c** 36.06

2 a 8.4   **b** 7.05   **c** 58.35   **d** 6.4   **e** 10.33
  f 95.93   **g** 10.52   **h** 73.17   **i** 55.34

3 a 77.33   **b** 79.63   **c** 21.24

4 90.4

5 a 3.3   **b** 22.16   **c** 2.12

6 a 6.2   **b** 21.38   **c** 14.8   **d** 31.43   **e** 46.15
  f 24.44   **g** 52.31   **h** 6.28   **i** 52.03

7 a 48.89   **b** 27.42   **c** 12

8 2.75 + 7.25; 0.75 + 9.25; 3.2 + 6.8; 6.85 + 3.15; 6.5 + 3.5; 3.65 + 6.35; 2.7 + 7.3; 5.5 + 4.5

2.3 Multiply and divide decimal numbers

1 a 4.5   **b** 2.4 × 2 = 4.8
  c 55, 1.1 × 5 = 5.5   **d** 72, 1.8 × 4 = 7.2
  e 264, 26.4   **f** 486, 24.3 × 2 = 48.6

2 a 1.3   **b** 8, 2.4 ÷ 3 = 0.8
  c 7, 3.5 ÷ 5 = 0.7   **d** 7, 2.8 ÷ 4 = 0.7

3 a 0.4   **b** 0.5   **c** 0.9   **d** 1.5   **e** 2.4
  f 2.0   **g** 3.6   **h** 7.5   **i** 0.4

4 a 76   **b** 83   **c** 456   **d** 367   **e** 350
  f 680   **g** 3740   **h** 7460   **i** 259

5 a 32   **b** 69   **c** 575   **d** 570   **e** 820
  f 5280   **g** 3480   **h** 348   **i** 789

6 a 3.6   **b** 7.2   **c** 1.54   **d** 2.83   **e** 0.56
  f 0.48   **g** 0.27   **h** 0.93   **i** 1.23   **j** 4.56
  k 67.89   **l** 54.32

7 a 4.9   **b** 8.4   **c** 1.76   **d** 3.74   **e** 0.48
  f 0.89   **g** 0.36   **h** 0.72   **i** 4.68   **j** 7.52
  k 37.64   **l** 48.21

8 17.08 × 6 = 102.48; 567.25 ÷ 5 = 113.45; 443.1 ÷ 4.2 = 105.5; 9.23 × 12.06 = 111.3138

9 a 19.2   **b** 2.4   **c** 1.2, 1234, 19.2

2.4 Rounding decimals

1 a 5   **b** 6   **c** 3   **d** 3   **e** 1   **f** 5

2 a 5.43 → 5.4   5.17 → 5.2   5.73 → 5.7   5.24 → 5.2
  5.06 → 5.1   5.55 → 5.6   5.92 → 5.9   5.64 → 5.6
  b 46, 45, 45   **c** 45.6, 45.3, 45.3

3 a any two of: 7.5, 7.6, 7.7, 7.8, 7.9
  (or these with any 2nd decimal place, e.g. 7.58, 7.91)
  b any two of: 8.4, 8.3, 8.2, 8.1
  (and with 2nd decimal place, e.g. 8.47, 8.06)
  c any two of: 3.35, 3.36, 3.37, 3.38, 3.39
  d any two of: 3.41, 3.42, 3.43, 3.44
  e 2.9, 3.7, 4.8
  f 5.51, 5.52, 5.53, 5.54

Don't forget!

* left
* two places; right
* The digits and decimal points are not lined up correctly

Exam-style questions

1 a $\frac{6}{10}$ or six tenths   **b** 6 or six

  c $\frac{6}{100}$ or six hundredths

2 34.67, 34.7, 34.76, 36.04, 36.47

3 a 25   **b** 16   **c** 30

4 a 15.3   **b** 36.5   **c** 41.1

5 a 88.18   **b** 33.62

6 a 3.5   **b** 3.5   **c** 0.5   **d** 4.8   **e** 0.6   **f** 18.4

7 a 71.778   **b** 5.6

8 a 240.5; 246; 239; 245   **b** 239, 240.5, 245, 246

3 Checking and approximation

3.1 Check solutions

1 a 4   **b** 36 ÷ 9 = 4 or 36 ÷ 4 = 9
  c 3 × 8 = 24 or 8 × 3 = 24   **d** 9 × 6 = 54 or 6 × 9 = 54
  e 90 − 34 = 56 or 90 − 56 = 34   **f** 44, 56 + 44 = 100

2 a 100; 100   **b** 120 − 60 = 60, 62
  c 600 − 500 = 100; 120   **d** 40 × 60 = 2400; 2537
  e 5 × 4 = 20; 18.72   **f** 30 ÷ 3 = 10; 8
  g 3 + 6 + 7 = 16; 15.7

3 a 216   **b** £51   **c** £494   **d** 270   **e** 82

4 a 7 × 3 = 21   45 ÷ 9 = 5   **b** 4 × 60 = £240
  c 80 ÷ 8 = £10

5 38.26 − 23.7

Don't forget!

* use rounding
* rounding; an inverse calculation
* subtraction
* any two of: 6 × 5 = 30, 30 ÷ 6 = 5, 30 ÷ 5 = 6

Exam-style questions

1 20 × 4 = 80 (or 21 × 4 = 84)

2 3.7 × 4.3 → 16; 32.786 − 22.098 → 10; 61.095 × 9.99 → 600; 359 ÷ 10.28 → 36

3 a 20 ÷ 5 = £4   **b** 8 × 10 = £80

4 a one of: 68.45 − 23.37; 68.45 − 45.08; 45.08 + 23.27
  b one of: 21.5 × 34.4; 739.6 ÷ 21.5 ; 739.6 ÷ 34.4
  c one of: 5.6 × 2.3; 12.88 ÷ 5.6; 12.88 ÷ 2.3

4 Fractions

4.1 Read, write and order fractions

1 a $\frac{1}{2}, \frac{1}{2}$ **b** $\frac{3}{4}, \frac{1}{4}$ **c** $\frac{2}{5}, \frac{3}{5}$

  d $\frac{7}{10}, \frac{3}{10}$ **e** $1\frac{1}{4}, \frac{3}{4}$ **f** $2\frac{1}{2}, \frac{1}{2}$

2 a–e one part shaded in each

3 $\frac{1}{10}, \frac{1}{5}, \frac{1}{4}, \frac{1}{3}, \frac{1}{2}$

4 a 4 parts shaded   **b** 2 parts   **c** 1 part
  d 3 parts   **e** 9 parts
  $\frac{1}{2}, \frac{2}{3}, \frac{3}{4}, \frac{4}{5}, \frac{9}{10}$

5 a $\frac{1}{7}, \frac{1}{6}, \frac{1}{5}, \frac{1}{4}, \frac{1}{3}, \frac{1}{2}$ b $\frac{2}{3}, \frac{4}{5}, \frac{5}{6}, \frac{7}{8}, \frac{9}{10}, \frac{11}{12}$

6 a $3\frac{1}{2}, 4, 4\frac{1}{2}$ b $1\frac{3}{4}, 2, 2\frac{1}{4}$ c $\frac{1}{6}, \frac{1}{7}, \frac{1}{8}$ d $\frac{5}{6}, \frac{6}{7}, \frac{7}{8}$

4.2 Use equivalent fractions
1 a $\frac{1}{2} = \frac{2}{4}$ b $\frac{3}{4} = \frac{6}{8}$ c $\frac{2}{3} = \frac{4}{6}$ d $\frac{2}{5} = \frac{4}{10}$

2 a $\frac{2}{4} = \frac{3}{6} = \frac{5}{10}$ b $\frac{2}{6}$ c $\frac{4}{10}$ d $\frac{6}{8}$

e $\frac{4}{6}$ f $\frac{4}{5}$ g $\frac{1}{3}$ h $\frac{3}{5}$

j $\frac{4}{8}$

3 a $\frac{4}{8} = \frac{8}{16}$ b $\frac{20}{30}$ c $\frac{9}{30}$

4 a $\frac{6}{8}, \frac{30}{40}$ etc.   b $\frac{10}{16}, \frac{50}{80}$ etc.   c $\frac{8}{10}, \frac{40}{50}$ etc.

4.3 Write fractions in their simplest form
1 a $\frac{1}{4}$ b $\frac{3}{5}$ c $\frac{4}{6} = \frac{2}{3}$ d $\frac{3}{9} = \frac{1}{3}$

e $\frac{6}{8} = \frac{3}{4}$ f $\frac{8}{10} = \frac{4}{5}$

2 a $\frac{1}{2}$ b $\frac{7}{10}$ c $\frac{4}{5}$ d $\frac{1}{2}$ e $\frac{3}{4}$ f $\frac{3}{4}$

3 $\frac{2}{3} = \frac{6}{9}, \frac{10}{20} = \frac{1}{2}, \frac{4}{5} = \frac{8}{10}, \frac{3}{4} = \frac{6}{8}, \frac{1}{4} = \frac{4}{16}$

4.4 Convert between fractions and decimals
1 a decimal: $0, 0.25, 0.5, 0.75, 1.0$; fraction: $0, \frac{1}{4}, \frac{1}{2}, \frac{3}{4}, 1$

b $\frac{1}{4} = 0.25$; $\frac{1}{2} = 0.5$; $\frac{3}{4} = 0.75$

2 a decimal: $0.1, 0.2, \ldots 0.9, 1$; fraction: $\frac{1}{10}, \frac{2}{10}, \ldots \frac{9}{10}, 1$

b $\frac{1}{10}$; 0.2; $\frac{4}{10}$; 0.9

3 a 0.2 b 0.6 c $4 \div 5 = 0.8$

d $1 \div 20 = 0.05$ e $3 \div 20 = 0.15$ f $21 \div 25 = 0.84$

4 $0.75, 0.4, 0.625, 0.8, 0.45; \frac{2}{5}, \frac{9}{20}, \frac{5}{8}, \frac{3}{4}, \frac{12}{15}$

5 a $\frac{4}{5}$ b $\frac{7}{10}$ c $\frac{4}{10} = \frac{2}{5}$

d $\frac{3}{20}$ e $\frac{19}{100}$ f $\frac{28}{100} = \frac{7}{25}$

6
Decimal	0.5	0.75	0.9	0.11	0.2	0.3
Fraction	$\frac{1}{2}$	$\frac{3}{4}$	$\frac{9}{10}$	$\frac{11}{100}$	$\frac{1}{5}$	$\frac{3}{10}$

4.5 Add and subtract fractions
1 a $\frac{4}{6}$ b $\frac{3}{10} + \frac{4}{10} = \frac{7}{10}$ c $\frac{2}{5} + \frac{2}{5} = \frac{4}{5}$

2 a $\frac{4}{5}$ b $\frac{8}{10} = \frac{4}{5}$ c $\frac{6}{8} = \frac{3}{4}$

3 a $\frac{3}{5}$ b $\frac{5}{10} = \frac{1}{2}$ c $\frac{3}{6} = \frac{1}{2}$ d $\frac{4}{9}$

4 a $\frac{10}{12} = \frac{5}{6}$ b $\frac{4}{12} = \frac{1}{3}$ c $\frac{8}{9}$ d $\frac{1}{11}$

4.6 Find fractions of quantities
1 a $\frac{2}{3}$ b $3 \times \frac{2}{10} = \frac{6}{10} = \frac{3}{5}$ c $2 \times \frac{2}{5} = \frac{4}{5}$

2 a $\frac{3}{8}$ b $\frac{4}{7}$ c $\frac{6}{10} = \frac{3}{5}$

d $\frac{12}{20} = \frac{3}{5}$ e $\frac{8}{15}$ f $\frac{10}{11}$

g $\frac{6}{7}$ h $\frac{15}{20} = \frac{3}{4}$ i $\frac{6}{9} = \frac{2}{3}$

3 a 8   b $12 \div 3 = 4$ c $20 \div 5 = 4$
d $20 \div 4 = 5$ e $20 \div 10 = 2$ f $18 \div 3 = 6$
4 a 4   b 5   c 5   d 3   e 4   f 4
5 a 6 apples in each crate
   b $30 \div 5 = 6, 6 \times 2 = 12, 6 \times 3 = 18, 6 \times 4 = 24$
6 a 15   b 28   c 40   d 9   e 18   f 20
7 a 45   b 90   c 100   d 405   e 24   f 32

Don't forget!
* a 6 parts shaded   b 10 parts shaded   c 6 parts shaded
* $\frac{3}{4} = \frac{15}{20}, \frac{2}{3} = \frac{20}{30}, \frac{1}{2} = \frac{15}{30}, \frac{1}{4} = \frac{5}{20}$

* Decimal	0.1	0.5	0.9	0.01	0.04	0.17
Fraction	$\frac{1}{10}$	$\frac{1}{2}$	$\frac{9}{10}$	$\frac{1}{100}$	$\frac{4}{100}$	$\frac{17}{100}$

* make a fraction out of 100; simplify
* divide by 5
* divide by 4; multiply by 3

Exam-style questions
1 a $\frac{5}{7}$ b $\frac{2}{8} = \frac{1}{4}$
2 a 7   b 6
3 a 24   b 12
4 a $\frac{1}{2}$ or $\frac{2}{4}$ etc.   b $\frac{4}{5}$
5 a $\frac{7}{10}$ b 0.25
6 a £10
7 $\frac{1}{5}, \frac{1}{4}, \frac{1}{2}, \frac{3}{4}$

5 Percentages
5.1 Decimals, fractions and percentages
1 a 5 columns (or rows)   b $8\frac{1}{2}$ columns (or rows)
   c 2 columns (or rows) and 3 squares
2 a decimal: $0, 0.25, 0.5, 0.75, 1$; fraction: $0, \frac{1}{4}, \frac{1}{2}, \frac{3}{4}, 1$;
   percentage: 0, 25%, 50%, 75%, 100%
   b decimal: $0, 0.1, 0.2, \ldots 0.9, 1$; fraction: $0, \frac{1}{10}, \frac{2}{10}, \ldots \frac{9}{10}, 1$;
   percentage: 10%, 20%, ... 90%, 100%
3 a $50\% = \frac{1}{2}$ b $\frac{1}{4} = 0.25$ c $75\% = 0.75$

d $10\% = \frac{1}{10}$ e $\frac{2}{10}\left(\frac{1}{5}\right) = 0.2$ f $70\% = 0.7$

4
Fraction	Decimal	Percentage
$\frac{3}{10}$	0.3	30%
$\frac{1}{4}$	0.25	25%
$\frac{9}{10}$	0.9	90%
$\frac{4}{10}$	0.4	40%
$\frac{8}{10}$	0.8	80%
$\frac{3}{4}$	0.75	75%

5 a 0.2, 20%   b $0.6, 0.6 \times 100 = 60\%$
   c $1 \div 20 = 0.05, 0.05 \times 100 = 5\%$
6 a 0.45   b 0.4   c 0.04
7 a $\frac{1}{5}$ b $\frac{11}{100}$ c $\frac{9}{100}$
8 a 55%, 75%, 12.5%, 37.5%   b 0.35, 0.8, 0.08, 0.15, 0.3, 0.09
   c $\frac{3}{10}, \frac{29}{100}, \frac{3}{100}, \frac{35}{100} = \frac{7}{20}, \frac{80}{100} = \frac{8}{10} = \frac{4}{5}, \frac{22}{100} = \frac{11}{50}$

9
Fraction	Decimal	Percentage
$\frac{7}{10}$	0.7	70%
$\frac{15}{20}$	0.75	75%
$\frac{2}{5}$	0.4	40%
$\frac{20}{40}$	0.5	50%
$\frac{17}{100}$	0.17	17%

5.2 Order and compare percentages
1 a $25\%, \frac{3}{10}, 0.35$ b $87\%, 0.89, \frac{9}{10}$ c $0.59, \frac{3}{5}, 63\%$
2 a $0.7, 74\%, \frac{3}{4}$ b $0.19, \frac{1}{5}, 21\%$ c $65\%, \frac{7}{10}, 0.72$

d 78%, $\frac{4}{5}$, 0.81 **e** 9%, $\frac{1}{10}$, 0.12 **f** $\frac{3}{20}$, 17%, 0.2

g 0.5, 53%, $\frac{11}{20}$ **h** 49%, 0.6, $\frac{5}{8}$ **i** 83%, $\frac{21}{25}$, 0.85

3 a 77%, 72%, 84%, 70%, 80%
   b science, RE, maths, English, art

5.3 Find percentages of quantities

1 a £30 **b** $65 \div 10 = 6.5$
   c $124 \div 10 = 12.4 = £12.40$ **d** £38.80
2 a £6 **b** £5.60 **c** £28.60 **d** 62 g **e** 340 ml
   f 45 cm **g** 70 km **h** 350 g **i** £400
3 a £6 **b** £20 **c** £15 **d** £3 **e** £28 **f** £6

4

Amount	10%	5%	15% of amount
£60	£6	£3	£9
£100	£10	£5	£15
£120	£12	£6	£18
£360	£36	£18	£54
£240	£24	£12	£36
£500	£50	£25	£75

5 a £4.50 **b** £10 **c** £8 **d** £12
   e £1.50 **f** £14 **g** £22 **h** £48
   i £30 **j** £64.80 **k** £84 **l** £150
6 50% of 50 = 10% of £250 = £25;
   25% of £120 = 10% of 300 = £30;
   20% of 100 = 5% of 400 = £20
7 a £3.50 **b** £10.50 **c** £12 **d** 46% **e** 80
8 a 50% **b** $\frac{1}{4}$
9 a £60 **b** £30 **c** $80 \div 4 = £20$
   d $80 \div 2 = £40$
   e 50% of 120 + 25% of 120 = 60 + 30 = £90
   f 50% of 80 + 25% of 80 = 40 + 20 = £60
10 clockwise from top: £90, £45, £135, £18, £36, £9, £27, £180
11 a £91 **b** $440 \times 75 \div 100 = £330$
   c $360 \times 85 \div 100 = £306$ **d** $450 \times 42 \div 100 = £189$
12 a £32
   b $\frac{2}{5}$ gives a price of £24; 25% reduction gives a price of £30;
   so $\frac{2}{5}$ off is better value
13 2 segments, 5 squares, 6 squares
14 a £10 **b** $£90 \div 10 \times 2 = £18$
   c $£45 \div 10 \times 2 = £9$ **d** $£75 \div 10 \times 2 = £15$
15 a £7.50 **b** £15 **c** £7.50 **d** £7
   e £25 **f** £22.50
16 a £8 **b** £4 **c** £2 **d** £14
17 £22; £132

Don't forget!

* 100% = the whole amount; $\frac{1}{2}$ price = 50% off; save 25% = $\frac{1}{4}$ off
* 10%, double

Exam-style questions

1 a 90% **b** 0.68 **c** $\frac{3}{4}$
2 a 72% **b** 0.06
3 0.7 75% $\frac{4}{5}$
4 a £9 **b** £7.50
5 a £5 **b** £80
6 £36
7 £9
8 £21
9 £3.60; £39.60

6 Money

6.1 Read and order amounts of money

1 a £3.85
   b £1 + £1 + 50p + 50p + 50p + 20p + 20p + 5p = £3.95
   c £1 + 50p + 50p + 50p + 50p + 20p + 20p + 20p + 10p
      + 10p + 5p + 5p = £3.90
   d £2 + £1 + 50p + 20p + 10p + 5p + 2p + 1p = £3.88
2 cream 83p, lettuce 90p, apples £1.30, cheese £1.75, eggs £2.08

3 a £22.50 **b** £18 **c** £60
   d £2.50 **e** £4.05 **f** £50.04 **g** £78.50
   h £329.51 **i** £3.80 **j** £2.02 **k** £570.92

6.2 Calculating with money

1 3.45 + 6.55 3.35 + 6.65 2.35 + 7.65 4.50 + 5.50
   1.25 + 8.75 4.35 + 5.65 5.15 + 4.85 9.05 + 0.95
2 a £40
   b £2.50 + £0.85 = £3.35
   c £12.50 × 2 = £25
   d 3 × £10 + £12.50 + £2.50 = £45
3 a £3.95
   b e.g. £2, £1, 50p, 2 × 20p, 5p or similar
4 a 25p
   b £1, 2 × 20p, 5p; 2 × 50p, 4 × 10p, 5p etc
   c Total = £5.20, so he is 20p short
5 a £27.50
   b 2745 × £0.15 = £411.75
   c 22 × £8 = £176
   d 9 ÷ 5, £1.80
6 a £9000 **b** £780 **c** £10.40 **d** £1.25 **e** £2.50
7 £560
8 a £20
   b 450 × 4 ÷ 100 = £18
   c 360 × 7 ÷ 100 = £25.20
   d 320 × 8 ÷ 100 = £25.60
9 a £960 **b** £49.50 **c** £10 800 **d** £210
10 a £60
   b £300; £1500 − £300 = £1200; £1200 ÷ 12 = £100 per month
   c £2500 − £500 = £2000; £2000 ÷ 8 = £250 per month
11 a £70 **b** £285
12 £375
13 a £34.29 **b** £61.11 **c** £9.62 **d** £73.33
   e £1.71 **f** £5.88
14 a £35 **b** £54 **c** £77 **d** £83
   e £185 **f** £366
15 a £27.30 **b** £12.80 **c** £72.50 **d** £835.50
   e £354.10 **f** £66.00
16 a £132
   b 33 × £12.75 = £420.75
   c £720 ÷ 80 = £9
   d £320 ÷ 14 = 22.857 142 86, £22.86
17 a £448 **b** £525 **c** £1855 **d** £1078
   e £22.40 **f** £11.36
18 a £600 **b** £12.25
   c any appropriate amounts totalling £80
19 a 3129 − 2572 = 557; 18 × 557p = 10 026p = £100.26
   b £0.11 × 180 = £19.80; £0.08 × 250 = £20; £39.80
20 £24.75; £9.50; £4.99; £39.24
21 £52.65

Don't forget!

* £3.04, £0.99
* wrapping paper → 5 × 2.50; Sally's hourly rate → 32.50 ÷ 5;
   250 min on the phone → 250 × 0.15;
   20% VAT on TV → 250 ÷ 10 × 2

Exam-style questions

1 £2
2 £5.50
3 £5.85
4 £7.05
5 a £7.20 **b** £10.80
6 £800
7 £9.30
8 £56.75
9 £10.20

7 Time

7.1 Read, record and measure time

1 a half past seven; 7.30 am, 07:30
   b quarter past six; 6.15 pm, 18:15
   c quarter to four, 3.45 am, 03:45
   d ten to nine, 8.50 pm, 20:50

2 a  08:20   **b** 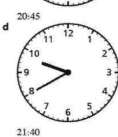 20:45

c 02:55   **d** 21:40

3 a 16:30, 05:20, 23:35, 09:50
b 9.30 am, 10.25 pm, 3.05 am, 4.44 pm
c 11.25 am, 11:25; 5.55 pm, 17:55

7.2 Use units of time

1 a 2 h 20 min **b** 30 min **c** 1 h 30 min **d** 3 h 55 min
2 a 2 h 5 min **b** 1 h 35 min **c** 1 h 45 min **d** 2 h 50 min
e 5 h 50 min **f** 2 h 45 min
3 a 09:25 **b** 57 min **c** 07:05 **d** 28 min
e 58 min; 59 min; 06:11 **f** 38 min
4 a Step: 1 h 10 min; Circuits: 45 min; Zumba: 1 h 15 min; Kettle Bells: 40 min
b 2 h 25 min **c** 11:45 **d** 25 min
5 Ben

7.3 Convert between units of time

1 a 12 **b** 1 hour = 60 minutes **c** 240
d 30 **e** 52 **f** 366
2 a 300 **b** 3
c 60 × 60 = 3600 **d** 416 ÷ 52 = 8
e 315 ÷ 7 = 45 **f** 72 ÷ 24 = 3
g 24 × 60 × 60 = 86 400
3 a 96 **b** 8 **c** 600
d 72 **e** 7 **f** 4
4 a 160 **b** 135 **c** 36 **d** 50

7.4 Use calendars

1 31, 28, 31, 30, 31, 30, 31, 31, 30, 31, 30, 31
2 a consecutive numbers starting on Saturday, finishing at 30
b Thursday **c** 18 June **d** 14 June
e 1st; 25 May **f** 25 − 2 = 23; 23 July **g** Monday

Don't forget!

* 3.15 pm → 15:15; 7.30 am → 07:30; ten past ten in evening → 22:10; ten to nine in morning → 08:50
* 4 h = 240 min; 36 months = 3 years; 7 weeks = 49 days; 5 min = 300 s; 48 h = 2 days; 3 h = 10 800 s
* Friday; Monday

Exam-style questions

1 a 2 h 45 min **b** 45 min **c** 3 h 30 min
2 19:35

3 a quarter past eleven **b** ten to five **c** twenty past six
4 a 09:55 **b** 46 min
c 27 min/19 min; Cheltenham to Bishop's Cleeve is quicker
5 a Wednesday **b** Sunday **c** 29 October
d 25 September **e** 17 November

98

8 Measures

8.1 Metric and imperial measures

1 a length: door, ribbon   weight: potatoes, cement   capacity: water, bottle
2 a cm, m **b** grams, kg **c** ml **d** km
e litres **f** grams
3 a 250 ml **b** 180 g **c** 16 m

4	Length/distance/height	Weight	Capacity
	miles, inches, feet, yards	stones, pounds, ounces	pints, gallons

5 a kilometre **b** inch **c** kilogram
d pint **e** metre **f** gram
6 a Sydney **b** Moscow
7 a 12°C **b** 22°C

8.2 Convert between metric units

1 a 3 cm **b** 7.5 cm **c** 60 mm **d** 25 mm
e 12.4 cm **f** 257 mm **g** 3 m **h** 3.5 m
i 3.54 m **j** 400 cm **k** 450 cm **l** 458 cm
2 a 4 km **b** 4.5 kg **c** 4.567 litres **d** 3000 m
e 5600 g **f** 2345 ml **g** 7200 m **h** 6 kg
i 7.2 litres
3 a 250 ml, 0.4 litres, 1800 ml, 2.5 litres
b 250 cm = 2.5 m
25 cm = 250 mm
0.25 km = 250 m
1250 m = 1.25 km

8.3 Add and subtract units of measure

1 a 69 mm **b** 77 mm **c** 7 m 65 cm
d 8 m 10 cm **e** 243 cm **f** 552 cm
2 a 854 cm **b** 255 g **c** 100 mm
d 1.3 km **e** 60 mm **f** 2 litres 800 ml
g 1 m 70 cm **h** 3 m 40 cm
3 a 5.7 m or 570 cm **b** 2.15 km **c** 600 ml or 0.6 litre
d 4.7 m or 470 cm

8.4 Read scales

1 a 2 **b** 5 **c** 20 **d** 100 ml **e** 250 g
2 a 1 litre 400 ml **b** 800 g
c 1 m 75 cm **d** 4.5 cm = 45 mm
3 a  **b**
c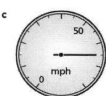
d
e
4 a 650 g; 1 litre 300 ml

b

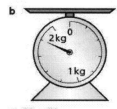

c 77 or 78 cm

8.5 Draw and measure lines and angles

Diagrams in the following section are not drawn to scale. Please check you have drawn the lines and angles in your own constructions accurately according to the instructions in the questions.

1 a 4 cm   **b** 6 cm   **c** 5 cm

2 a A ———————|———————— B

   b C ———————————|—— D

   c E ——————|————————— F

3 a 3 cm, 4 cm, 5 cm; AC

4

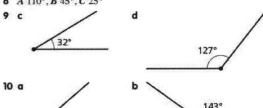

5 a acute   **b** obtuse   **c** obtuse

6 a 60°   **b** 150°

7 a 75°   **b** 125°   **c** 118°   **d** 23°

   e 136°   **f** 109°

8 A 110°, B 45°, C 25°

9 c

32°

   d

127°

10 a

42°

   b

143°

   c

162°

   d

48°

11

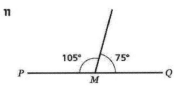

105°   75°

P ——————————— Q
    M

Don't forget!

* degree → angle, temperature; gram → weight; litre → capacity; mile → distance/length; ounce → weight; inch → distance/length; kilometre → distance/length; cm → distance/length; pint → capacity
* 90°, acute
* 90°, 180°
* multiply; divide

Exam-style questions

1 a 5 cm   **b** 45°

2 a 4 litres   **b** 95 mm

3 6 m 55 cm

4 a 9 cm   **b**

52°

C ——————— D

5 a cm or metres   **b** litres   **c** grams

6 a 1 m 25 cm   **b** 1 kg 200 g   **c** 750 ml

9 Area and perimeter

9.1 Perimeter of rectangles

1 a 5 cm + 7 cm + 5 cm + 7 cm = 24 cm

   b 12 m + 3 m + 12 m + 3 m = 30 m

   c 26 cm + 14 cm + 26 cm + 14 cm = 80 cm

2 a 178 cm   **b** 33.6 m

3 a 20 cm   **b** 29.6 cm

4 a 80 m   **b** 170 cm

5 a 12 cm   **b** 6 cm

6 42 + 20 = 62 cm; 23 − 12 = 11 cm; 62 + 23 + 20 + 11 + 42 + 12 = 170 cm

7 116 cm

8 60 cm

9.2 Area of rectangles

1 a 6 cm²   **b** 4 × 6 = 24 m²   **c** 5 × 3 = 15 mm²

2 a 18 cm²   **b** 20 m²   **c** 6 mm²

3 a 27.28 m²   **b** 45 cm²

Don't forget!

* add width and length, then double the total
* multiply the width by the length

Exam-style questions

1 a 16 cm   **b** 12 cm²

2 a 22 cm   **b** 18 cm²

3 44 cm

10 Volume

10.1 Volume of cuboids

1 a 8 cm³   **b** 12 cm³   **c** 3 × 2 × 4 = 24 cm³

2 a 30 cm³   **b** 240 cm³   **c** 3300 cm³

3 a 86 625 mm³   **b** 100.44 m³   **c** 98.716 cm³

4 a $l = w = h = 1$ cm, $V = 1$ cm³;

     $l = w = h = 2$ cm, $V = 8$ cm³;

     $l = w = h = 3$ cm, $V = 27$ cm³;

     $l = w = h = 4$ cm, $V = 64$ cm³;

     $l = w = h = 5$ cm, $V = 125$ cm³;

     $l = w = h = 6$ cm, $V = 216$ cm³;

     $l = w = h = 7$ cm, $V = 343$ cm³;

     $l = w = h = 8$ cm, $V = 512$ cm³;

     $l = w = h = 9$ cm, $V = 729$ cm³;

     $l = w = h = 10$ cm, $V = 1000$ cm³

   b 5 cm

   c 10 m

Don't forget!

* multiply length × width × height
* all its edges are the same length

Exam-style questions

1 90 cm³

2 64 m³

3 108 cm³

11 Tables and charts

11.1 Read and interpret real-life charts

1 a Boris, Juli   **b** Mori   **c** Juli

   d Ali   **e** Ali, Boris

2 a

	Boys	Girls	Total
Y10	64	56	120
Y11	65	72	137
Total	129	128	257

   b 17

   c 1

   d add numbers in inner box

3

Gloucester			
86	Birmingham		
184	98	Liverpool	
302	216	118	Carlisle

Gloucester to Liverpool = 86 + 98 = 184;
Birmingham to Carlisle = 98 + 118 = 216;
Gloucester to Carlisle = 86 + 98 + 118 = 302

4 a 90 miles   **b** 39 miles
  c Durham and Newcastle   **d** 110 miles
5 a 64 miles   **b** 116 − 103 = 13 miles
6 a 4.8 km   **b** 4 miles
  c 16 + 8 = 24 km   **d** 200 miles
  e 80 + 16 + 6.4 = 102.4 km   **f** 30 miles
7 a $6   **b** £5   **c** $900   **d** $163.50
8 a £12.75   **b** £17   **c** £23.80
9 a July   **b** January   **c** June and September
10 a 12:25   **b** 37 min   **c** 23 min

11.2 Read bar charts and dual bar charts

1 a 8   **b** 21   **c** 4   **d** £6   **e** 67
2 a higher; Girls   **b** Y10 and Y11
  c Boys: 40−50, approx. 48; Girls: 60−70, approx. 62; total approx. 110
  d 55   **e** 45
3 a 100   **b** 305

11.3 Draw bar charts

1 red: 3 squares; blue: $2\frac{1}{2}$; black: 5; silver: 4; white: $1\frac{1}{2}$ squares

2 pineapple: 6 squares; melon: $3\frac{1}{2}$; peach: $4\frac{1}{2}$; strawberry: $7\frac{1}{2}$; plum: 2

3 a strawberry   **b** 21   **c** plum   **d** 8

Don't forget!

* they are an important part of understanding information in real-life
* Bar chart → Results of a survey; Distance chart → In a road atlas; Conversion chart → Currency exchange; Information table → Library opening times
* how much; 4; 1

Exam-style questions

1 a supermarket   **b** 15   **c** 58
2 elephant: 10 squares; lion: 8; tiger: 7; crocodile: 5; snake: 2
3 a 6 cm   **b** 5 cm   **c** London
  d Brisbane, Vancouver   **e** Brisbane
4 a 82 miles   **b** 41 miles   **c** 56 miles   **d** 278 miles
5 a Saturday   **b** 08:30 − 16:30
  c 4 hours   **d** Friday
6 a $9.30   **b** £8   **c** $31   **d** $186
7 a 47.5 g   **b** 6   **c** 950 g   **d** 20

Practice Paper

Section A (Calculator)

1 a 11 cm   **b** 65−70°
2 a
  −5 −4 −3 −2 −1 0 1 2 3 4 5
  b 2   **c** −3
3 90 cm³
4 a 8   **b** 5   **c** clarinet
5 a 6700 ml   **b** 5.06 m
6 a £39.42   **b** £10.58
7 a 27   **b** 6   **c** 11
8 a Wednesday   **b** 3rd May
9 a 36 cm²   **b** 50 cm
10 £18
11 a 7.5   **b** 7.8
12 a metres or yards   **b** ml or (fluid) ounces
13 a 124 miles   **b** 110 miles   **c** 165 miles
14 a 08:45   **b** 9 min   **c** 32 min
15 782 units; £39.10
16 a 40 km   **b** 15 miles   **c** 320 km
17 a Peru   **b** Canada

Section B (Non-Calculator)

1 athletics: 6 squares; swimming: 5; cycling: $7\frac{1}{2}$; sailing: $3\frac{1}{2}$; gymnastics: $4\frac{1}{2}$
2 a 37.2   **b** 643   **c** 7300   **d** 7.2
3 a eight hundred and thirty-six
  b 800
4 a 544   **b** 117
5 a   **b** 19:50

6 £2.50
7 a $\frac{7}{11}$ **b** $\frac{4}{8}\left(\text{or } \frac{1}{2}\right)$
8 a 0.1   **b** 70%   **c** $\frac{3}{5}$
9 a £3   **b** 10
10 a 8, 39, 40, 54, 109, 122
  b 0.09, 0.79, 7.07, 7.2, 8.9, 9.8
  c −10, −3, −1, 0, 4, 7
11 a 50 × 20 = 1000   **b** 42.61 − 24.56 or 42.61 − 18.05
12 a 1 kg 600 g or 1.6 kg   **b**